CIRIA C703

Crane Stability on Site

an introductory guide

John Laing Construction Limited
and
Sir William Halcrow & Partners Ltd.

Department of Trade and Industry

sharing knowledge
∎
building best practice

Summary

Cranes are some of the most useful and widely operated items of plant on construction sites - from the small housing site to the multi-million-pound building or civil engineering project.

However, if misused, they can cause serious harm. There is no other item of construction equipment which has the capacity for causing as much damage or injuring so many people as does a crane in an accident.

Most serious accidents involving cranes are a result of inadequate planning and unsafe use leading to instability and overturning.

All site engineers, managers and supervisors who are involved in the specification, installation or use of cranes on site, must be aware of the fundamental criteria, planning issues and checks that are needed to ensure lifting operations proceed in a logical, safe and stable manner.

It is the purpose of this guide to bring together, in a single volume, the main points which need to be considered to ensure that a crane remains stable at all times. The guide's main focus is **stability in use** - it does not attempt to cover the design of cranes or all aspects of the lifting operation; these are adequately covered in other publications.

Crane Stability on Site is divided into five main sections:

■ Section 1... deals with management and planning and gives the legislative background. The basic principles of loading, ground conditions and foundation design are also covered;

■ Section 2... describes mobile cranes and their stability requirements in detail;

■ Section 3... covers tower cranes and their foundations;

■ **Section 4...** considers some special situations and other lifting appliances that may be encountered on site;

■ **Section 5...** provides important information about the inspections that are required and the documentation that should be in place.

An appendix gives a typical calculation for the foundation of a mobile crane. Accident case studies are also presented so that the reader can learn from previous situations.

Throughout the site guide extensive reference is made to other relevant documents which may deal with a particular topic in more detail. These references have been compiled into a comprehensive bibliography at the back of the guide.

The site guide concludes with a list of useful contacts, a glossary of terms and a subject index.

Crane Stability on Site

CIRIA C703, London

First published as SP131 1996 © CIRIA, 2nd edition 2003 ISBN 0-86017-703-3

Keywords	Reader interest	Classification	
mobile cranes tower cranes stability safety foundations	site engineers site managers site supervisors client representatives students	Availability Content Status User	unrestricted advice/guidance committee guided construction professionals

Published by CIRIA, Classic House 174-180 Old Street, London EC1V 9BP UK.

Acknowledgements

CONCEPT

Crane Stability on Site is the output from CIRIA Research Project RP541. It is one of the series of site guides produced under CIRIA's Programme Advisory Committee for Construction Operations.

RESEARCH CONTRACTOR

This guide was produced by staff from Laing Civil Engineering, Sir William Halcrow & Partners, Laing Plant Division and Halcrow Fox.

Project Supervisor & Editor	David Lloyd	Laing
Consultation Coordinator	David Slater	Halcrow
Crane Consultant	Tim Watson	Laing
Text and Diagrams	Nick Cook	Laing
	Bob Dunkley	Laing
	Mike Evans	Laing
	Jason Fairall	Laing
	Bernard Holman	Laing
	Andrew Homes	Laing
	Neil Smith	Laing
	Rod Nicholls	Halcrow
Graphic Design and Layout	Trevor Good	Halcrow Fox

This document was updated in May 2003 by Mr P Oram, in consultation with Steering Group members, to take into account the Lifting Operation and Lifting Equipment Regulations (LOLER) 1998.

COPYRIGHT

FINANCIAL CONTRIBUTIONS

The research project was funded by the DoE Construction Sponsorship Directorate, CIRIA's Core Programme and the Institution of Civil Engineers Research and Development Enabling Fund.

Acknowledgements

PROJECT STEERING GROUP

CIRIA, Laing and Halcrow wish to express their appreciation to the Project Steering Group which guided the work, supplied some of the source material and made valuable contributions in reviewing and agreeing the text. The group comprised:

Rod McClelland (Chairman)	Alfred McAlpine Construction Ltd
Elizabeth Bowman	W S Atkins plc
Peter Branton	Construction Industry Training Board
David Butterworth	Health & Safety Executive
Les Hancock	Taywood Engineering Ltd
Mike Harrison	Health & Safety Executive
Bob MacGrain	Baldwins Industrial Services
Jim Saville	Liebherr GB Ltd
Paul Smith	Health and Safety Executive
Antony Thompson	Safety Assessment Federation
Chris Watson	Tarmac Construction Engineering Services
Martyn Wenger	Sir William Halcrow & Partners Ltd
Peter Woodhead	Department of Environment

CIRIA's Research Manager for the project was Dr Ghazwa Alwani-Starr

SOURCE MATERIALS

CIRIA is grateful to the following organisations whose guidance documents were used for reference during preparation of this guide:

Ainscough Crane Hire Ltd	Costain Building and Civil Engineering Ltd
Amec Civil Engineering Ltd	John Glover Ltd
Association of Lorry Loaders, Manufacturers & Importers	Grove Europe Ltd
British Standards Institution	Health & Safety Executive
Building Research Establishment	ICI Engineering Department
Building Employers Confederation	Manitowoc Europe Ltd
Construction Industry Training Board	NCK Ltd
Construction Plant Hire Association	R-B International plc

Contents

Contents

Introduction and Scope

Construction efficiency and productivity is greatly assisted by the use of cranes and other forms of lifting appliances. Over the years bigger, better and more sophisticated cranes have become available and, when properly used, they are an invaluable tool.

However, if a crane is incorrectly positioned or installed, overloaded or otherwise misused then the consequences can be disastrous. Potentially the most dangerous incident is instability leading to overturning and it is this eventuality that this guide aims to prevent.

> **Research has shown that overturning is the most frequently occurring type of mobile crane incident.**

Overturning incidents occur with unnecessary regularity for both lorry-mounted mobile cranes and crawler cranes. Although overturning incidents involving tower cranes are less common, the consequences are often more severe. This guide therefore covers all the main types of crane that will normally be encountered on site.

Information is given on loading, ground conditions, foundation details and hazards that need to be avoided.

Reference is made to the legislation and other authoritative documents which govern the use of cranes on site.
The management and planning aspects, which are a prerequisite of a safe working environment, are outlined.

> **"One of the most important documents for persons concerned with cranes is BS7121."**   **HSE 1996**

This guide is **not** intended to cover all aspects of lifting operations, crane usage or crane manufacture - it is focused on maintaining the stability of the crane whilst on site.

The guide does not cover the use of cranes for demolition, earthworks (eg draglines) or their conversion for use as piling rigs; albeit many of the principles of loading, ground conditions and foundation design apply in these situations.

Derricks, pedestal cranes and overhead travelling cranes are also excluded.

The guide is split into five main parts:

Section 1 **The Fundamentals.** This section introduces the important management and planning aspects which are necessary for maintaining the stability of cranes on site. The legislative background is given and then the basic principles of loading, ground bearing and foundation design are summarised;

Section 2 **Mobile Cranes.** This section covers the various types and sizes of lorry-mounted cranes, crawlers and lorry-loaders. There is useful advice on the strategy for various ground conditions;

Section 3 **Tower Cranes.** This section covers all the main types of tower cranes and concentrates on the types of base and foundations required;

Section 4 **Special Cases.** Descriptions and particular precautions for some of the less common situations are given, together with details of telescopic handlers, yard cranes and excavators used as cranes;

Section 5 **Checklists and Documentation.** This section gives guidance on the inspections to be carried out to ensure that the crane is set-up correctly and remains stable during use.

Appendices give an example of a mobile crane support calculation and some case studies of past accidents.

Introduction and Scope

Throughout this guide references to relevant British Standards, various authoritative documents and other sources of information may be found at the end of each topic within solid boxes as above.

The titles in these boxes may appear in shorthand form, but the full titles can be obtained from the comprehensive bibliography at the back of the book.

KEY TO SYMBOLS

Particular points of emphasis are marked with exclamation marks

 Situations where specific calculations are required by a competent designer are indicated by the calculator sign.

Examples of incidents involving crane instability are indicated by the accident sign.

Safety on site is every individual's responsibility. If you see something that looks wrong then make sure that something is done about it.

The Fundamentals   1

INTRODUCTION

Before using any crane on site it is important to understand the basic organisational and technical issues which will help to ensure that the crane remains stable throughout its duties. This section of the guide brings together the basic principles based on legislation, relevant British Standards and other guidance documents which cover the safe use of cranes on site.

> **You are also advised to refer to your own company/site rules and procedures which will translate these principles into specific actions and responsibilities at your place of work.**

Part	Contents
1.1	**Management**
1.2	**Legislation**
1.3	**Planning**
1.4	**Loading**
1.5	**Ground Conditions**

1.1   The Fundamentals - Management

1.1.1   GENERAL

As with all other operations on site, effective management of lifting operations will ensure safety and efficiency.

> **Management Principles**
>
> - Plan
> - Resource
> - Communicate
> - Monitor

All lifting operations, whether large or small, complex or simple must be controlled by establishing a safe system of work, as required by the Health and Safety at Work etc Act 1974.

1.1.2   SAFE SYSTEM OF WORK

In principle all safe systems of work for crane operations are identical and should include the following:

- planning the operation;
- selection of the correct crane and associated equipment;
- maintenance of the crane and associated equipment;
- selection of appropriately trained and competent personnel;
- provision of adequate, properly trained and competent supervision;
- provision for the safety of those involved in, and others who may be affected by, the operation;
- effective communication between all of the relevant parties;
- ensuring that all necessary test certificates and other documents are in order and available;
- preventing unauthorised movement or use of the crane and equipment.

Selection of Personnel

All those involved in the team effort of a lifting operation must be:

- competent;
- adequately trained and/or supervised;
- able to communicate clearly;
- unimpaired by alcohol or drugs;
- aware of their duties.

The individual duties of crane drivers, slingers, signallers, maintenance personnel etc, may be found in BS 7121 Part 1 – General, and subsequent parts for specific types of crane.

 A mobile crane overturned when the load swung erratically during slewing and swung out of the safe working radius. The stand-in crane driver, who was operating the crane, was inexperienced.

In order to ensure the implementation of the safe system of work **one person** should be appointed to have responsibility for, and overall control of, the lifting operation. This person is referred to as the "**Appointed Person**" in BS7121 but may have another title in practice eg Lifting Manager.

1.1.3   THE APPOINTED PERSON

The Appointed Person's duties include:

■ assessment of the lifting operation in terms of planning, choice of crane and equipment, and liaison with other parties affected by the lift;

■ ensuring that inspection and maintenance has been carried out;

■ ensuring that there is an effective procedure for reporting defects and incidents and taking any necessary corrective action.

■ Organisation and control of all lifting operations.

The Appointed Person must have:

- **adequate training and experience to enable these duties to be carried out competently;**
- **the authority to stop the operation in the event of an unacceptable safety risk.**

1.1.4   DELEGATION OF DUTIES

Some of the duties, but not the responsibilities, of the Appointed Person may be delegated where considered appropriate. For a simple lifting operation it may be appropriate, for example, to brief the slinger/signaller on the operation and appoint him/her to control the lift.

The duties of the Appointed Person should not be delegated to the crane driver.
(The driver is required to be at the controls when handling loads and is therefore not in a position to take overall control of the operation.)

It is the responsibility of the Appointed Person to ensure that the duties of each individual involved in lifting operations are clearly defined and communicated with no gaps or overlaps.

1.1.5   CRANE MAINTENANCE

To ensure that the crane is in satisfactory operating order at all times, there are various periodic inspections, tests and thorough examinations that must be undertaken.

For full details of the requirements see BS 7121 Part 1 – General, and subsequent parts for specific types of crane.

 It is important to ensure that enough time is allowed for the necessary inspections and tests to be carried out properly.

 A telescopic jib mobile crane overturned as a result of overloading. The Automatic Safe Load Indicator was not working.

1.1.6   CONTRACTUAL RELATIONSHIPS

It is important to ensure that the wide variety of contractual arrangements used in the construction industry do not compromise the organisation and control of lifting operations.

Any organisation which requires a load to be moved by crane, and does not have its own cranage, has two basic options - hiring a crane or employing a Contractor to carry out the lifting operation.

 If an individual or organisation does not have expertise in lifting operations they should not hire cranes but should opt for the Contract Lift option.

 Before entering into a contract, Employing Organisations have a duty to satisfy themselves that the Contractor has the necessary competence to carry out the work.

Responsibilities for insurance, whether in terms of the crane, the load or third parties may also need to be clarified.

```
┌─────────────────────────┐
│    EMPLOYING            │
│    ORGANISATION         │
├─────────────────────────┤
│ The organisation requiring the │
│ load to be moved        │
└─────────────────────────┘
```

HIRED CRANE
(Hired and Managed)

The Employing Organisation must:

■ carry out all work in accordance with BS71221

■ supply the "Appointed Person"

■ plan the lift and operate a safe system of work

■ ensure that the crane hired is of a suitable type and capacity

■ check the credentials of the crane hire company and certification supplied

The crane owner has a duty to:

■ provide a crane that is properly maintained, tested and certificated

■ provide a competent driver.

CONTRACT LIFT
(Fully Contracted)

The Employing Organisation should specify:

■ that all work is to be undertaken in accordance with BS71221

■ that the contractor is to supply the "Appointed Person"

■ what information and/or services will be provided to the Contractor by the Employing Organisation

The Contractor is responsible for:

■ supplying the "Appointed Person"

■ planning the lift and operation of a safe system of work

■ organisation and control of the lifting operation.

1.1 The Fundamentals - Management

1.1.7 Expert Advice

The Appointed Person may require specialist advice when planning and organising the lifting arrangements; for example, where temporary works are required to support the crane. The Appointed Person may need input from competent engineers and designers to ensure that:

- the crane is of adequate capacity;

- there has been an accurate assessment of ground conditions;

- the foundations for the crane have been designed and checked properly;

- the foundations are constructed in accordance with the design and are inspected prior to loading.

A mobile crane overturned while lifting a load within its capacity when the 125mm thick, reinforced concrete hard-standing under one outrigger collapsed. The driver had been told that the hard-standing was adequate to support the crane.

If the crane is to be temporarily supported on or, in the case of a tower crane, tied to the permanent works structure, then the **permanent works designer** should be consulted to ensure that the proposals are adequate and acceptable.

1.1.8 Sources of Information

In order for the Appointed Person, and those with delegated duties, to make informed decisions about crane siting and support requirements it is important to gather all available information.

- Information on crane capacity and accurately calculated outrigger/track/foundation loads should be sought from the crane manufacturer direct or via the hirer.
The advice of a crane engineer may be required to assist in sizing the crane.

- Information regarding ground conditions on site may be available from existing site investigation data. If not, then further investigation in the form of trial pits, excavations or boreholes will be required (see Section 1.5.2).

- To check for underground hazards it may be necessary to approach local utility companies, the highway authority and adjacent building owners.

- Most soil mechanics books contain information regarding earth bearing pressures and settlements for different soil types. Simple basic information on foundations and ground conditions is provided in Section 5 of BS 5975 Code of Practice for Falsework.

- The Construction (Design and Management) Regulations place duties on the Client and Designer to obtain, and make available to the Planning Supervisor, information relating to the site. The Planning Supervisor may therefore be able to provide information about any existing site investigation data including details of ground investigations, identified underground services or other hazards to crane operations not included in the original pre-tender health and safety plan.

REFERENCES

BS 5975
BS 7121 Parts 1,2,3,4 and 5
CDM Regs and Approved Code of Practice
Construction Safety Manual
Lifting Operations and Lifting Equipment Regulations 1998
CITB *Construction Site Safety*
CIRIA *Site Safety Handbook*

> There are various statutory requirements which apply to lifting operations; the following being the main items:

THE HEALTH AND SAFETY AT WORK ETC. ACT, 1974, is very widely drawn and places duties on those who design, manufacture, import, supply, erect, install, provide, control and use any plant or equipment for use at work. Employers must also ensure the provision and maintenance of plant, equipment and systems of work which are safe and without risks to health.

THE SUPPLY OF MACHINERY (SAFETY) REGULATIONS, 1992 places duties on manufacturers and suppliers of plant and equipment to:

- ensure that equipment is of a safe design
- provide instructions for safe use.

THE PROVISION AND USE OF WORK EQUIPMENT REGULATIONS, 1998 (PUWER) requires that plant and equipment:

- is suitable for its intended use
- is properly maintained
- is used by people who are adequately trained.

THE MANAGEMENT OF HEALTH AND SAFETY AT WORK REGULATIONS, 1999 (MHSW) require that the risks associated with any work activity are assessed so that the necessary preventative and protective measures can be identified and put into place. The stability of cranes during lifting operations is one of the factors to be considered.

THE CONSTRUCTION (DESIGN AND MANAGEMENT) REGULATIONS, 1994 (as amended) place duties on clients, designers, planning supervisors, principal contractors and contractors to focus on health and safety matters throughout all stages of a construction project - from conception, design and planning through to the execution of works on site and subsequent maintenance, repair and demolition. Lifting operations should be covered in the Health and Safety Plan and, where required, information provided by the various parties such that factors influencing crane stability can be assessed at a sufficiently early stage.

THE LIFTING OPERATIONS AND LIFTING EQUIPMENT REGULATIONS, 1998 (LOLER) replaced all previous regulations specifically dealing with lifting, including the Construction (Lifting Operations) Regulations, 1961. LOLER applies to all lifting operations wherever the Health and Safety at Work etc, Act applies, and are goal setting rather than prescriptive, as was the case with previous lifting regulations. The regulations cover all aspects of the selection, installation, use, inspection, thorough examination and maintenance of lifting equipment, together with the management of all lifting operations. An Approved Code of Practice and Guidance from the HSE (L113) provides practical guidance on the requirements of LOLER and the lifting related aspects of MHSW and PUWER.

As well as these overriding pieces of legislation which apply to lifting operations in general, there is more specific guidance in various British Standards, HSE Guidance Notes and other documents referenced throughout this book.

 One of the most important documents for people concerned with cranes is BS 7121: 1989, "Code of Practice for Safe Use of Cranes" which is referred to in the guidance to LOLER. Part 1 covers general matters, whilst Parts 2, 3, 4 and 5 deal with inspection, examination and testing; mobile cranes; lorry loaders and tower cranes respectively. This Standard requires the establishment of a management system for the safe use of cranes and stresses the importance of thorough planning in all lifting operations.

1.3 The Fundamentals - Planning

> **All lifting operations must be planned in advance to ensure that the most suitable arrangement is put into operation and that all hazards and risks have been identified and addressed.**

1.3.1 RISK ASSESSMENT

Legislation requires that risk assessments are carried out for all work operations in order to identify any significant risks. Where a significant risk is found to exist, then measures must be taken to remove or to minimise it.

Where lifting operations are concerned it is important to start the risk assessment process early in the planning of the work as it may be possible to make the operation inherently more safe for very little extra effort.

Examples:
- *When working in city centres, arrange for lorry access onto site so that there is no public interface when lifting off the load.*
- *When working adjacent to a public highway, organise the works so that crane jibs always face away from, or are parallel to, the road.*

A mobile crane overturned while off-loading sheet piles from a delivery lorry outside the site.

Risk assessment should be used as a tool to assist the planning process. Do not start the risk assessment after all the key decisions have been made.

REFERENCE

The Management of Health and Safety at Work Regulations 1999

1.3.2 CRANE OPTIONS

Each type of crane has certain features making it more suitable for a particular application.

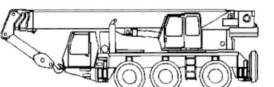

■ Telescopic mobile cranes are suitable for short duration operations and where mobility around or on/off site is important (for details see Section 2).

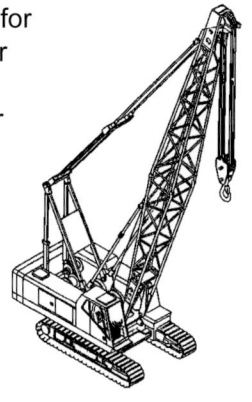

■ Crawler cranes are more suitable for longer duration operations, and for operations where pick and carry duties and routine movement over relatively short distances are necessary. Crawler cranes are generally uneconomic for short site visits due to the high mobilisation and demobilisation costs associated with transport, rigging and derigging (for details see Section 2).

■ Tower cranes provide coverage over large areas whilst taking up little room at ground level on site.
Elevated control cabins allow operators excellent views of lifting operations, increasing efficiency and safety.
Relatively high mobilisation and foundation costs restrict their use to longer term operations (for details see Section 3).

1.3.3   CRANE CHOICE

The choice of a suitable crane is governed by the following factors for each lifting operation:

- The characteristics of the load to be lifted;

- The selection of suitable lifting gear. Remember that the weight of the lifting gear must be taken into account when sizing the crane;

- The crane position, where the load is to be lifted from, the route that the load will take during the lift and where it will be landed;

- Erection and dismantling constraints;

- Site and environmental constraints.

SITE AND ENVIRONMENTAL CONSTRAINTS

- Ground conditions;

- Underground hazards:
  - open or backfilled excavations
  - services
  - drainage pipes
  - tunnels
  - basements;

- Overhead cables;

- Distance of the crane from the structure under construction, adjacent buildings, roads and pedestrian accesses from which clearance must be maintained;

- Prevailing weather conditions and exposure of the site:
  - wind loading
  - ice and snow loading;

- Route to, and access on to the site, for the crane and vehicles delivering the load;

- Space for final positioning and safe operation of the crane:
  - deployment of the outriggers
  - room for slewing;

- Clearance to railway tracks and overhead catenaries;

- Clearance to aircraft in the vicinity of airfields (Aircraft warning lights may be required).

1.3.4 METHOD STATEMENTS

The production of a written method statement is one of the most important of the Appointed Person's duties because:

- it demonstrates that a safe system of work has been established;

- it will record and highlight any residual risks and how they are to be addressed;

- it defines the method of lifting and ensures that a suitable crane is specified and used;

- it provides a basis for the communication of the lifting plan to other members of the team.

A crawler crane overturned, because of an overload, when the method of work was changed by the supervisor without consultation. The method statement was ignored.

The success of the lifting operation is dependent on a clear and thorough method statement effectively communicated to all personnel.

REFERENCES

Construction Methods and Planning: Illingworth
BS 7121 Parts 1,3 & 5

1.4 The Fundamentals - Loading

The three basic factors affecting the stability of a crane in use are:

- Load combinations and their relation to the centre of gravity of the crane

- The support arrangement
  - ground conditions
  - foundations
  - any tying in arrangements

- Operator control

Before moving on to the ground conditions and support arrangements it is worth considering the basic loading on cranes.

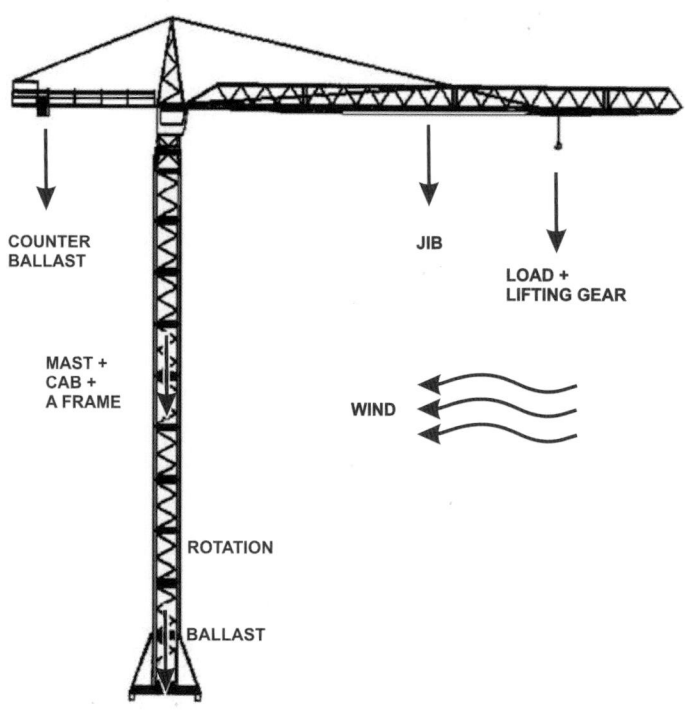

COUNTER
BALLAST

JIB

LOAD +
LIFTING GEAR

MAST +
CAB +
A FRAME

WIND

ROTATION

BALLAST

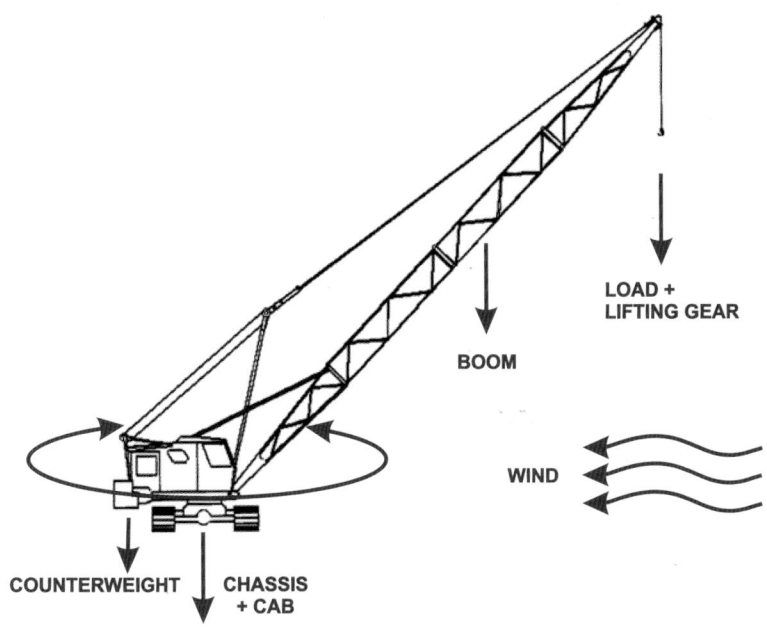

LOAD +
LIFTING GEAR

BOOM

WIND

COUNTERWEIGHT | CHASSIS
                     + CAB

TYPICAL LOAD COMPONENTS

- weight of the crane

- weight of the lifting gear

- weight and position of the load

- wind loading on crane and load

- impact loading (e.g. caused by an incorrectly slung load slipping)

- displacement of vertical load, and introduction of lateral loading, if the crane is not level (due to incorrect set-up or differential settlement of supports)

- centrifugal load (caused by slewing or a swinging lifted load).

Always find out or calculate the weight of the load to be lifted.
DO NOT guess and DO NOT use the crane as a weighing scale.

TYPICAL MAXIMUM IN-SERVICE WIND SPEEDS

- ▪ Tower cranes   20m/s (45mph)

- ▪ Crawler cranes 14m/s (31mph)

- ▪ Mobile cranes 9.8m/s (22mph)

For specific limitations on the crane in use you should check with the manufacturer. Operational limitations may well be lower than these figures, eg when handling loads with a large wind area such as wide formwork panels.

 A 10 ton mobile crane overturned while unloading steel plate frames when a freak gust of wind moved the load out of radius.

 Before signboards or decorations are fitted to any crane, the manufacturer's agreement should be obtained. The additional weight and wind loading area need to be taken into account when assessing the support arrangements.

In order to determine the support arrangements required for a crane, be it a mobile or a tower crane, it will be necessary to gather some information about the ground conditions on site.

It is necessary to know:

- the character of the ground
- the water conditions
- the engineering properties of those strata relevant to the design of the foundations
- the location of any underground hazards.

 Where there is any doubt as to the adequacy of the ground, further advice should be sought from a specialist Geotechnical Engineer.

1.5.1   SITE CATEGORIES

Sites can be categorised to highlight the most likely potential problems that need to be considered. More attention is required to establish the strength of the ground where ground conditions are poor or where there is a lack of data on the nature of the sub-soil.

Typical site categories are:

Greenfield sites

- No previous construction activities.
- Problem areas are: adjacent to rivers, estuaries and flood plains where soft alluvial deposits and high ground water tables can be expected.

Beaches

- Low sand density and/or high/variable water table create difficult conditions.

1.5　The Fundamentals - Ground Conditions

Filled construction sites (Brownfield sites)

- Unknown previous conditions, eg basements, poorly filled open pits, storage tanks, variable and badly compacted fill.

Paved areas

- These can look deceptively strong but may have been laid on weak ground underneath.

- If a road is used regularly by heavy commercial vehicles and shows no signs of distress then it will be less of a concern than a lightly trafficked carpark or estate road.

- Footpaths always demand further investigation as there may be weaker material or shallow services underneath thin surfacing.

- Edges of paved areas are usually weak.

Town centre sites

- Expect underground hazards eg basements, sewers, tunnels, live services, poorly backfilled trenches, manholes, inspection chambers etc.

 Records of accidents due to crane instability show that problems have occurred in almost all site conditions. Care is required in all situations.

The catastrophic result of an outrigger jack punching
through weak surfacing.

1.5   The Fundamentals - Ground Conditions

1.5.2 GROUND INVESTIGATION

Soil conditions may vary widely between sites or even within a single site.

Some initial site observations, local knowledge and any existing site investigation reports will indicate the likely amount of additional investigation needed to evaluate the soil conditions so that support arrangements for the crane can be properly assessed.

The principles for site investigations for foundations for tower cranes are the same as those for site investigations for the foundations of permanent works. However, the foundations for mobile cranes are set at the ground surface and hence the investigation should pay special attention to the character of the ground at shallow depths.

Further information on site investigation practice can be obtained from BS 5930 and BS 1377. An outline of the methods used for routine investigations is given in annex G of BS 5975.

Soil descriptions and consistency

GRANULAR	COHESIVE
Very loose - SPT < 4 blows/300mm	Very soft - c_u < 20 kN/m²
Loose - SPT 4–10 can be loosened with a spade easily; 50mm wooden peg can be easily driven	Soft - c_u 20–40 can be moulded easily by light finger pressure
Medium - SPT 10–30 can be excavated with a spade with effort	Firm - c_u 40–75 can be moulded by strong finger pressure.
Dense - SPT 30–50 requires pick for excavation; 50mm wooden peg hard to drive	Stiff - c_u 75–150 cannot be moulded by fingers; can be indented by thumb
Very dense - SPT > 50 steel pin hard to drive	Very Stiff - c_u > 150 can be indented by thumb nail
SPT = Standard penetration test	c_u = Undrained (immediate) shear strength

Before a crane arrives on site existing information on the nature of the soils should have been studied, any additional site investigations required should have been carried out and warnings of any specific hazards should have been incorporated in the Health & Safety Plan.

1.5.3   GROUND BEARING CAPACITY

The bearing capacity of the ground can be referred to in two different ways, ultimate bearing capacity or allowable bearing pressure.

Ultimate bearing capacity - The value of gross loading intensity for a particular foundation at which the resistance of the soil to displacement of the foundation is fully mobilised, ie failure.

Allowable bearing pressure - The maximum allowable loading intensity at the base of the foundation, taking into account the ultimate bearing capacity, the amount and kind of settlement expected, and the ability of the structure to accommodate this settlement.

A factor of safety of three on the ultimate bearing capacity value to derive the bearing pressure should normally be adopted for tower crane foundation design.

For mobile cranes a lower factor of safety may be more appropriate (see Section 2.5.2).

1.5.4   SETTLEMENT

For all cranes it is very important that they are set up level and plumb and remain so during use. It is therefore critical when assessing the support requirements that excessive or differential settlement does not occur.

The settlement of free-draining granular soils occurs virtually instantaneously as the soil is stressed by the load from the crane, and therefore most of the settlement may well take place during erection of the crane.

In the case of impermeable clay soils, there is potential for immediate settlements to occur in the short term under undrained conditions, and for long term consolidation settlements associated with gradual dissipation of the excess pore water pressures generated by the sustained load under a crane foundation.

For the normal short term use of a mobile crane these long term consolidation settlements will not be critical. For mobile cranes remaining in-situ for long periods the daily checks and adjustment of crane level carried out by the operator will compensate.

For tower crane foundation design, long term consolidation settlement should be considered.

REFERENCES

BS 5975   BS 5930   BS1377   BS 8004
CIRIA: *Site Guide for Foundation Construction*

INTRODUCTION

Mobile and crawler cranes are in daily use on most sites, and there is a wide variety of types and capacities.

This section of the handbook starts with some descriptions of the main types of mobile and crawler cranes that will be encountered and then goes on to describe in some detail the factors that need to be taken into account to ensure that the crane remains stable.

Advice is given on providing suitable foundations for mobile crane outriggers.

> Mobile and crawler cranes are sometimes mounted on floating craft for marine operations. This is a specialist operation which is not covered in this handbook.
> If you are involved in such work you should seek further advice.

Part	Contents
2.1	Types of Crane
2.2	General Considerations
2.3	Loading Cases
2.4	Ground Conditions
2.5	Foundations
2.6	Final Siting Checks

Definition of terms used

The diagrams below show the various components of a crawler crane and a mobile telescopic crane.

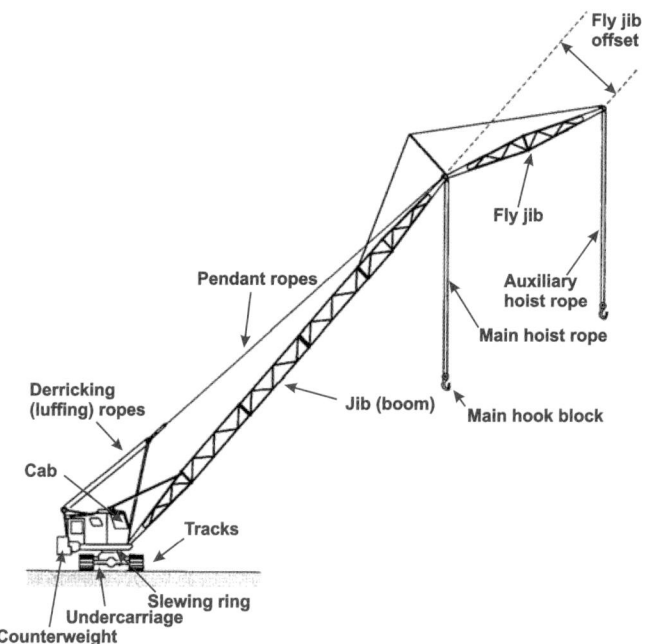

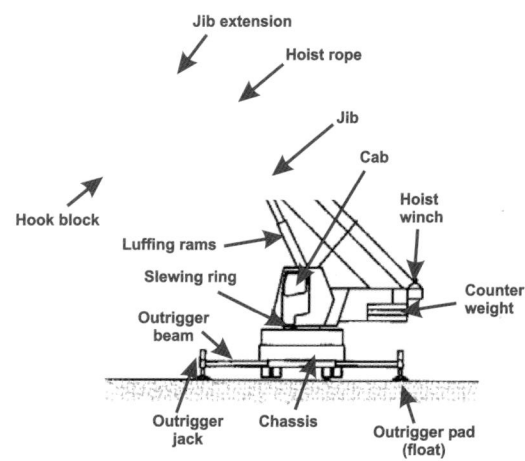

2.1.1 LORRY-MOUNTED TELESCOPIC

Typical capacities between 15 and 1000 tonnes

A very versatile piece of equipment which can travel to site on the public highway and in general be positioned, rigged and in use in a very short time. Larger lifting capacity machines will take longer, as items such as additional counter weights, boom and outriggers may be delivered on separate lorries.

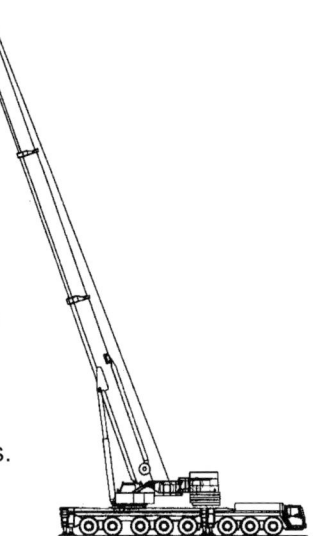

Stability for these machines is achieved with the use of outriggers. Great care must be taken when planning the position of these cranes as it is vital that the outriggers are founded on good ground.

 All outriggers should be fully extended and all tyres should be clear of the ground unless the crane is constructed and certified for reduced outrigger base duties, in which case each outrigger should be extended to the length specified by the manufacturer, and the appropriate lifting capacity chart utilised.

Most lorry-mounted telescopic cranes can be supplied with fly jibs, and some larger versions can be equipped with luffing fly jibs.

2.1.2 ROUGH TERRAIN TELESCOPIC

Typical lifting capacities in the range of 10 to 50 tonnes.

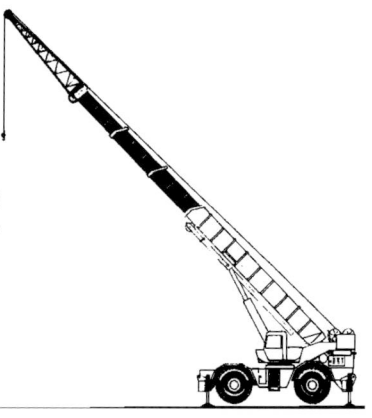

These cranes are very similar in principle to the lorry mounted telescopic cranes, with the exception that they are designed with high ground clearance which enables them to move easily around the construction site between lifting operations. They may have "crab" steering which makes them very manoeuvrable on congested sites.

Some rough terrain cranes may not be allowed to travel on the public highway.

 Outrigger deployment and levelling of the machine must be to the manufacturers instructions.

Where the crane is of suitable design, loads can be transported around site by rough terrain mobiles. The lifting capacity is reduced and the **"PICK AND CARRY"** ratings must be applied. During **PICK AND CARRY** operations it is important that the load is carried according to the manufacturer's instructions; often the load must be carried over the front of the vehicle with the slewing ring locked (see Section 2.3.3).

2.1.3 ALL TERRAIN TELESCOPIC

These are similar to lorry-mounted telescopic cranes.
They possess good road-going capabilities but have axles
and suspension which can cope with less well prepared
site access. However, with the larger machines the ground
conditions will need to be checked before running on site.

When in use their operation is as for lorry-mounted
telescopic mobile cranes.

 **Outrigger deployment and levelling of the
machine must be to the manufacturers
instructions.**

Most all terrain cranes can be fitted with fly jibs and luffing
fly jibs.

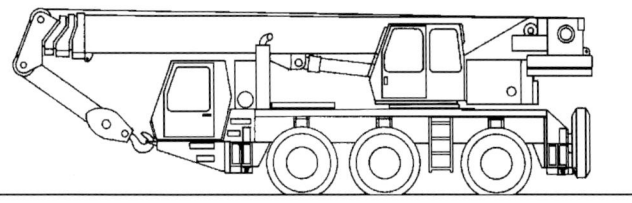

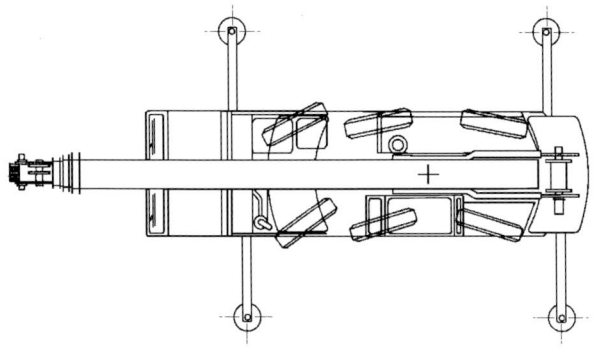

2.1.4 CRAWLER CRANES

Typical lifting capacities in the range of 15 to 250 tonnes.

As the name suggests, these cranes are mounted on a track laying chassis not wheels. Movement around site is very easy because the tracks enable them to travel over uneven ground and manoeuvre into tight working areas. The working surface must be level and capable of supporting the bearing pressures exerted by the tracks.

Crawler cranes can be used to travel with a suspended load, but the travelling surface must be level and free from any underground hazards. Operation must be according to the manufacturer's instructions.

One advantage of the crawler crane over lorry-mounted mobiles is that they can generally be moved around site between lifting positions fully rigged.

As with the previous machines there are various additional jib configurations such as fly jibs or luffing fly jibs.

2.1.5   LATTICE JIB CRANES

Typical capacities between 450 and 1500 tonnes.

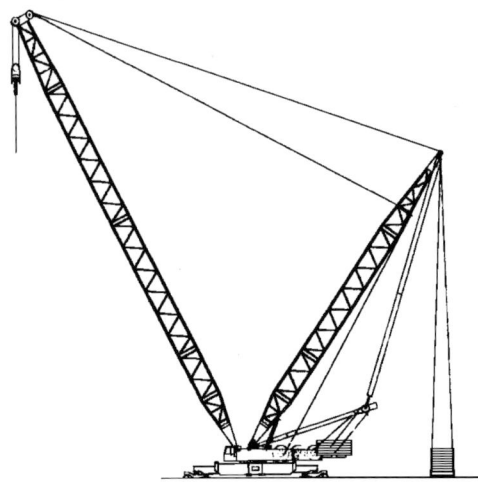

This type of crane is basically the same as the lorry-mounted mobile, with the exception of the jib which, as the name suggests, is constructed of an open-latticed steel structure. Generally this construction is used for the very largest lorry-mounted cranes, there being a considerable saving in the weight of the jib which would otherwise detract from the safe working load.

Erection takes considerably longer as the jib is not self erecting, and will require the use of another crane (probably a lorry-mounted telescopic jibbed crane).

Stability is by the use of outriggers, which, because of the size of the machines, will be delivered on a separate vehicle. All outriggers should be deployed according to the manufacturer's instructions and the appropriate lifting capacity chart used. All tyres should be clear of the ground.

Lorry-mounted lattice jib cranes can be supplied with fly jibs and luffing fly jibs.

2.1.4 LORRY LOADERS

Typical lifting capacity of the range 0.5 to 10 tonnes

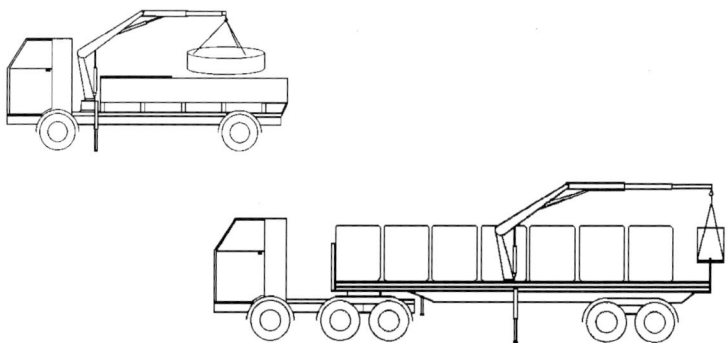

A lorry loader is a crane mounted on a commercial truck chassis with the primary function of loading and unloading the payload.

The loaders are hydraulically powered with the pump operated from the lorry engine. The booms can be extended and articulated to position the hook over the load to be moved.

Stability of the system is again vital and no load can be moved without first extending the outriggers which are usually fixed to the lorry chassis.

As the crane is hydraulically operated pressure relief valves can be utilised to prevent overload.

REFERENCE

BS 7121 Part 4: Lorry Loaders

Further information on the operation of lorry loaders can be obtained from the Association of Lorry Loaders Manufacturers and Importers (see page 112).

2.2.1   ACCESS

Getting the required crane into the correct position to carry out the lifting operation must be given careful consideration.

Large capacity lorry-mounted cranes can be in excess of 19m long and although they have multi-wheeled steering may not easily be positioned on a congested site. Special access may need to be provided, both for the crane and the high capacity trailers now in common use for delivering the crane counterweights and jib sections.

Having positioned the base machine it may be necessary to position another smaller crane adjacent to it so that the small crane can offload and assemble the larger machine's outriggers, counterweights and jib sections.

When working in city centres, the operation of moving the crane onto site will dictate careful advance planning with police and local authorities and possible overnight working.

 Do not forget when planning cranage operations that lay down areas for the load or parking positions for delivery vehicles will probably be needed.

2.2.2   POSITIONING OF CRANES

Extreme care must be taken when setting up and using a crane, especially in the following circumstances:

■ On or adjacent to public highways:

This will require close liaison with police and local authorities and possible overnight working.

2.2 Mobile and Crawler Cranes
– General Considerations

A careful check should be made for underground services which could be damaged by the crane's loading, and other underground hazards which could affect the crane's stability. Temporary bridging over, or diversion of, the services may be needed.

 The location of all underground services must be determined when planning lifting operations.

REFERENCE

HSE Guidance HS(G) 47

■ **Adjacent to railways:**

Railway authorities insist that a crane must be positioned such that, if the crane were to collapse, neither the jib nor load can fall within 3 metres of the track.

Work close to a railway will normally be carried out during a rail closure and it may be that the crane cannot even be moved into position or rigged until the closure commences.

> **When working adjacent to a public highway or railway an independent design check may be required, proving that the scheme has been planned and engineered such that no damage will occur to existing structures, property or to the public.**

■ **Near overhead power lines:**

Cranes must never be positioned in the exclusion zone around overhead electricity cables. This is to prevent arcing to earth through the crane structure.

Lifting operations close to electricity cables or pylons may have to be scheduled during power off conditions.

All overhead electric lines on site must be clearly marked, and barriers erected, to ensure that no item of mobile plant can approach too close to the line.

> **REFERENCE**
> HSE Guidance Note GS6

■ **Next to an existing building:**

Care must be taken to ensure that there is adequate room for slewing, including regulation clearances and correct deployment of outriggers.

A check should be made for basements which may need temporary propping (see also section 2.6 of this guide).

If a crane is to be positioned on, or next to an existing structure a design calculation check will be required to establish whether or not temporary strengthening or propping is needed.

A mobile crane overturned into an eight metre deep excavation when an outrigger sank through the old floor on which it was supported.

2.2 Mobile and Crawler Cranes
– General Considerations

■ **On previously disturbed ground:**

A check should be made for underground hazards and poorly backfilled excavations.

> *A telescopic mobile crane overturned when the outriggers sank into a recently back filled trench.*

Do not forget that frozen ground can give a false sense of security.

■ **Adjacent to open excavations:**

If a crane has to be positioned, or manoeuvred, next to an open excavation then stability checks will need to be carried out on the slope of the soil or the capacity of the retaining system (see section 2.6 of this guide).

2.2.3 USE

The supporting surface under the tracks or outrigger pads must be level and firm to support the weight of the machine and its load.

It is frequently necessary to provide an increased bearing area under outrigger pads and sometimes this is also necessary under the tracks of crawler machines (see Section 2.5).

When using outriggers always extend the beams to the manufacturer's instructions and lower all the jacks to lift all the tyres clear of the ground.

If blocking must be built up under outriggers to obtain a level machine, ensure it is stable, covers sufficient area, and will not topple or sink into the ground.

 Do not lift if the "out-of-level" of the machine exceeds the manufacturer's limits.

Excessive side loads on the jib can cause overloading. Side loads can result from:

■ lifting when not level

■ slewing when not level

■ dragging a load

■ sudden acceleration or deceleration of slewing

■ excessive wind speeds

 Extreme care must be taken when travelling with or without a load (see Sections 2.3.3 and 2.3.4).

REFERENCE

BS 7121 Part 3: Mobile Cranes

2.3 Mobile and Crawler Cranes – Loading Cases

This section describes the way in which the loadings on the foundations under the crane vary.

2.3.1 MOBILE CRANE

The stability of a mobile crane whilst lifting is dependent on the correct deployment of outriggers.

As the crane slews around, the outrigger loads will increase and decrease. The maximum loading may occur:

- under the laden jib

- under the counterweight, generally with a light lift or no load

- under the jib when rigging the crane, eg when picking up a long fly jib.

The manufacturers should be consulted for each case.

An unloaded mobile crane overturned while setting up for a lift. One outrigger had been left unextended.

LADEN   UNLADEN

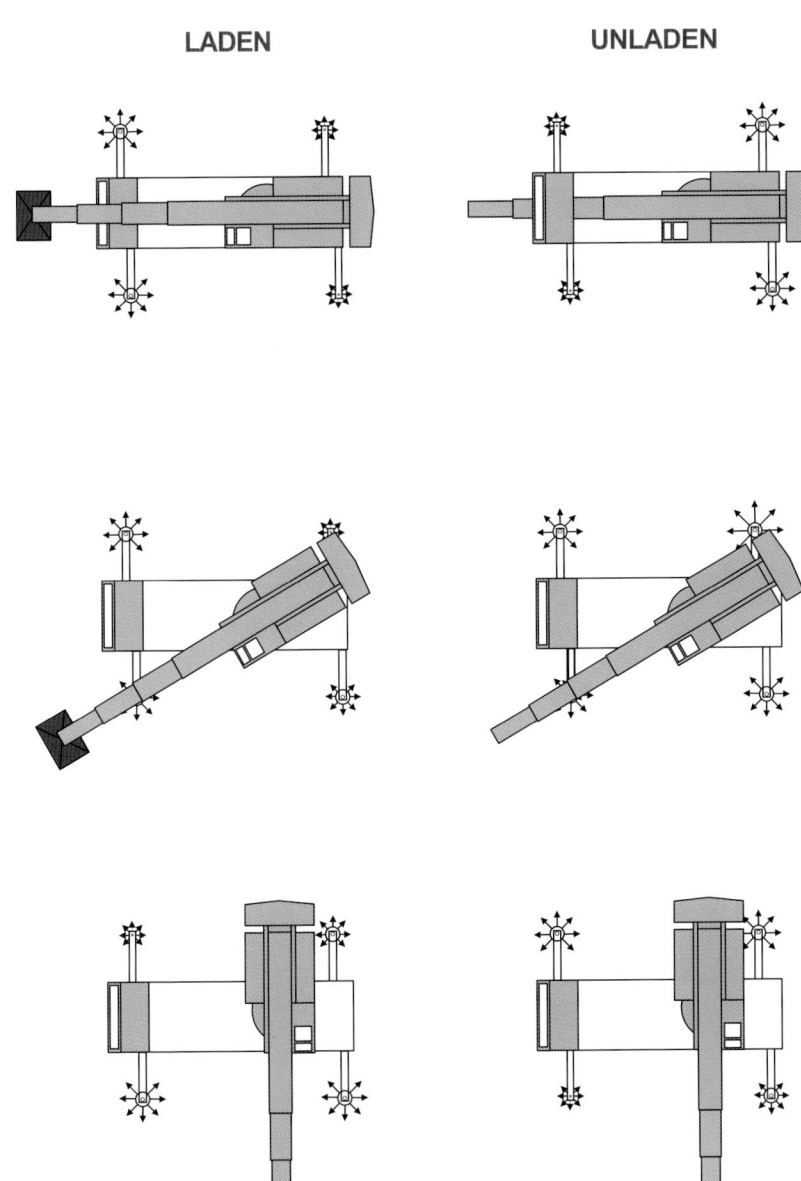

2.3 Mobile and Crawler Cranes - Loading Cases

2.3.2 CRAWLER CRANES

Loading from the crane is
resisted by the ground
pressure under the tracks.
If the jib is in line with the
tracks there will be an equal
triangular or trapezoidal
loading under each track.

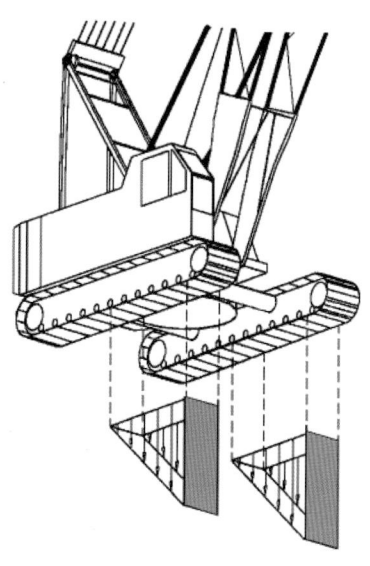

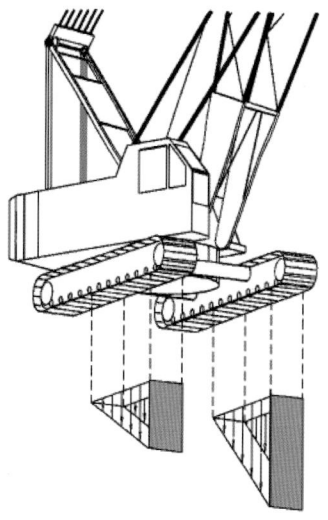

As the jib is slewed around
until it is over the end of one
track the pressure increases
under that track.

If the jib continues to slew until it is at right angles to the tracks the pressure now becomes a rectangular distribution with the track nearest to the load having the greatest pressure.

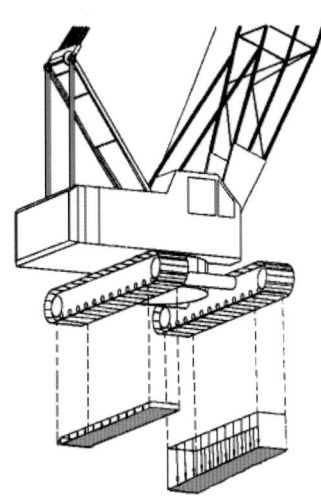

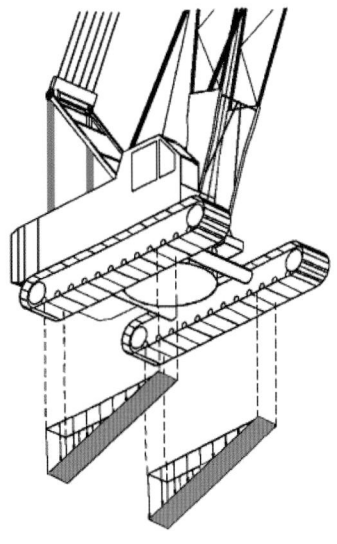

 With no load on the hook block, the pressure may be higher under the rear of the tracks due to the counterweight.

2.3 Mobile and Crawler Cranes - Loading Cases

2.3.3 SAFE TRAVELLING WITH LOADS

Travelling with a suspended load is dependant on many variables:

- ground conditions;
- jib length;
- fore and aft / sideways swinging of the load;
- acceleration and deceleration of travel speed.
- Careful planning is essential if travelling with a load.

DO NOT

- Travel with the maximum SWL;
- Travel with a load up, down or across inclines;
- Travel over uneven, unstable or uncompacted ground;
- Travel rough terrain cranes with the load over the side;
- Make erratic movements, such as starting/stopping suddenly.

DO

- Operate to the manufacturer's instructions;
- Check whether the jib has to be in line with the direction of travel;
- Check tyre pressures on rough terrain cranes;
- Use shortest jib possible;
- Use tag lines to control the load;
- Keep load close to the ground.

A rough terrain crane overturned while travelling up a 5° slope carrying a load that was only 20% of the safe working load at that radius. Soft ground caused the crane to tilt and then overturn.

Extreme caution must be exercised when travelling with loads. Any ground irregularities, travel speed variation or shock loads will increase the effective radius of the load.

2.3.4 SAFE TRAVELLING ON INCLINES

Cranes must only be travelled on inclines when unladen.

Extreme care must be exercised when travelling cranes up, down or across inclines. Telescopic jibs should be positioned as per the manufacturer's instructions; generally fully lowered into the transport position.

Crawler crane jibs should also be positioned as per the manufacturer's instructions; generally at a low angle when climbing inclines (to avoid any possibility of the crane toppling backwards) and at a steep angle when descending inclines (to avoid any possibility of the crane toppling forwards).

A mobile telescopic crane running free on wheels and unloaded, overturned while being moved. The slewing pin was not securely in place and when the crane was travelling the camber was sufficient to cause the crane jib to slew through 90° and the crane to overturn.

2.4 Mobile and Crawler Cranes
- Ground Conditions

2.4.1 BEARING CAPACITY

To determine the size and type of timber mat, grillage or other type of foundation required, it is necessary to make an assessment of the ground bearing capacity.

 Where there is any doubt as to the adequacy of the ground, further advice should be sought from a specialist Geotechnical Engineer. *Basic advice on ground assessment is given in section 1.5.*

A further confirmation of the strength of the ground is to observe the amount of rutting which occurs when a roadgoing heavy goods vehicle is driven onto site. If the wheels sink into the ground, or traction is difficult, then the ground is obviously towards the weaker end of the scale.

Be extremely careful when assessing areas overlain with paving or hardcore.

 Although the surface may appear strong there is a risk that an outrigger will punch through into weaker material beneath. If in doubt, make the assessment based on the underlying material and ignore the surfacing.

Water tends to reduce the strength of soils and this should be considered during the assessment, especially if the area is in a tidal or floodwater area.

On large construction sites where mobile cranes are going to be in common use over long periods, a site survey should be undertaken to identify soil types and underground hazards.

With the results of the investigation it may be possible to improve some areas, if required. Ground improvement can take many forms and the equipment already in use on the site will have a significant influence on the choice of method adopted.

When all surveys are completed, any hazards identified and soil improvements completed, a site layout can be produced identifying danger areas, access corridors and safe working areas for the types of mobile cranes to be used.

 Crane access zones and corridors should be clearly delineated by markers and shown on a plan of the site in the Health and Safety plan

REFERENCE

The Construction (Health, Safety and Welfare) Regulations 1996

2.4.2 SETTLEMENT

Settlement during operation must be kept to a minimum in order for the crane to be kept level within the manufacturer's tolerances.

Excessive settlement is critical because if the slewing ring of the crane is not horizontal, the jib will not be in a vertical plane. This will cause side loads on the jib which could cause the jib to fail and which may exceed the capacity of the slewing gear.

Also, excessive settlement may attract additional load onto the outrigger or track that is settling.

2.4 Mobile and Crawler Cranes
- Ground Conditions

If practicable the following procedure should be followed before general lifting proceeds:

1.   Lift the load approximately 150mm and hold for a period over one outrigger at maximum radius.

2.   Inspect the outrigger foundation for signs of settlement or punching.

3.   If excessive settlement occurs then either the crane must be repositioned on stronger ground or the outrigger foundations increased in size.

2.4.3 UNDERGROUND HAZARDS

The following are some of the underground hazards which may be encountered on a typical construction site:

- electricity cables;
- gas/water/drainage pipes;
- culverts;
- uncompacted material;
- covered shafts and manholes;
- recently backfilled excavations and trenches;
- voids under old concrete foundations;
- cellars and basements.

A mobile crane was operating with one outrigger founded on the top of concrete plinth. The plinth was hollow and settled about 50mm, causing the load to swing out of radius and the crane to topple.

46

2.5.1 OUTRIGGER LOADS

A survey of major crane manufacturers' quoted figures concluded that the following values are the maximum theoretical loads on each support for typical mobile cranes:

30 tonne capacity truck-mounted telescopic:	33 tonnes
50 tonne capacity all-terrain telescopic:	40 tonnes
80 tonne capacity all-terrain telescopic:	61 tonnes
120 tonne capacity all-terrain telescopic:	80 tonnes
160 tonne capacity all-terrain telescopic:	95 tonnes

 The above figures are for guidance only. For accurate outrigger loadings for your particular application, consult the crane manufacturer direct or via the hirer.

2.5.2 OUTRIGGER FOUNDATION AREA

The area of the pad attached to the outrigger of a mobile crane is relatively small and therefore generates high pressures on the ground.

$$\text{PRESSURE} \quad = \quad \frac{\text{LOAD}}{\text{AREA}}$$

Most soils will not be capable of resisting these pressures so a method of increasing the foundation area under the pad is required. The simplest way is to place some form of spreader mat between the pad and the soil.

The area of mat required can be determined from first principles using the data and guidance given in relevant British Standards and Soil Mechanics books.

However, for mobile cranes **up to 160 tonne capacity** the charts which follow may be used to define the area of mat or foundation required.

FACTORS OF SAFETY (FOS)

The charts on pages 49 and 50 give foundation areas for a range of Factors of Safety against bearing failure and excessive settlement of the ground.

FOS of 3.0 is more normally used for permanent works foundations and will give a conservative size of foundation area. It should be used for outrigger foundations where minimum ground information is available, where soils are variable or where minor settlements could be critical to a precision lifting and placing operation.

FOS of 2.0 is adequate for most situations.

FOS of 1.5 is the absolute minimum and should only be used where ground conditions have been accurately identified under the guidance of an experienced geotechnical engineer.

For further guidance on the choice of Factor of Safety for your particular application you should refer to your Company Engineering and/or Safety Department.

For an example of the application of these charts see the Typical Calculation given in Appendix A1 of this book.

 For larger cranes, special situations and where ground conditions are not straightforward (eg layered strata, paved areas, etc) the foundation must be specially designed by a competent engineer experienced in this type of work.

OUTRIGGER FOUNDATION AREAS ON GRANULAR SOILS

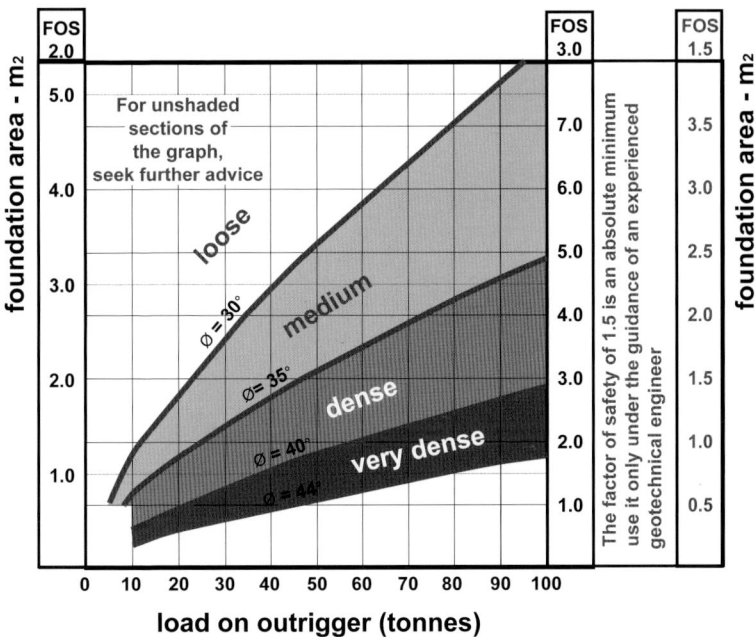

Ø   =   Angle of Internal Friction

FOS   =   Factor of Safety (see notes on page 48)

 If only general information on the soil type is available use the upper limit of the bands shown.

 Where groundwater is at a depth B or less below the level of the foundation, or the site is liable to flooding, then the above foundation areas should be doubled. *(B is the width of the foundation)*

OUTRIGGER FOUNDATION AREAS ON COHESIVE SOILS

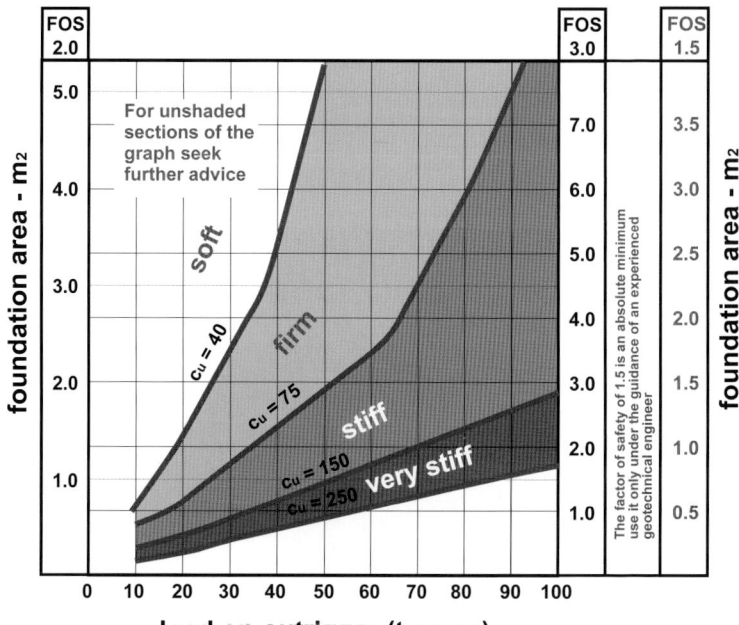

c_u = Undrained Shear Strength

FOS = Factor of Safety (see notes on page 48)

 If only general information on the soil type is available use the upper limit of the bands shown.

 If the site is liable to flooding then the above foundation areas should be increased by 50%.

 If the foundation is NOT approximately square in plan, but is rectangular then the above foundation areas should be increased by 10% (B/L should not exceed 0.5 where B is the width of the foundation and L is the length of foundation).

2.5.3   Outrigger Foundations

Various methods of providing an increased area of foundation under the outrigger pad may be used.

It is generally the responsibility of the user/site to supply these materials, unless otherwise agreed with the crane hirer.

 Foundation materials must be designed to spread the load over the area required.

The material used to form the spreader mat must be strong enough to spread the outrigger load over the full foundation area. Design calculations are required to be sure of the load that can be safely carried. Even without calculation, commonsense dictates that some arrangements are totally unsuitable. For example, a sheet of ply or broken scaffold board may provide the foundation area required but would have insufficient strength to spread the load.

 A mobile crane overturned while well within its safe working load. Although the four outriggers were fully extended, one was supported on a rotten sleeper and sank into the ground, which was uneven and disturbed.

Timber Mats

These consist of a grillage of sleepers or other thick timbers. This is suitable for most situations commonly encountered, but loading is limited by the strength of the timber (see Appendix 1 for example calculation).

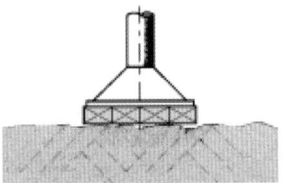

2.5   Mobile and Crawler Cranes - Foundations

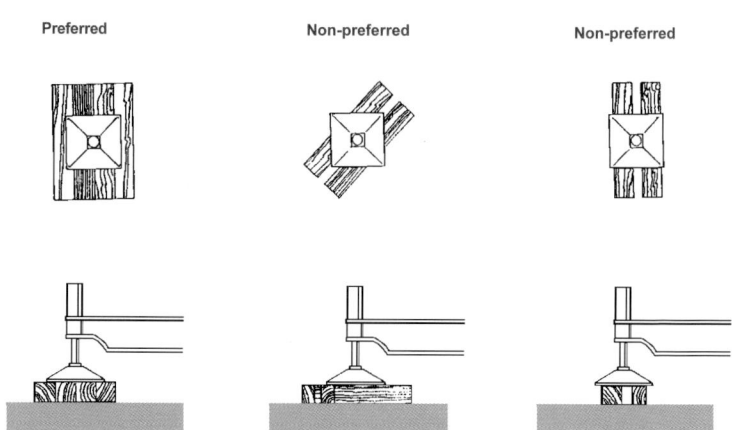

Preferred | Non-preferred | Non-preferred

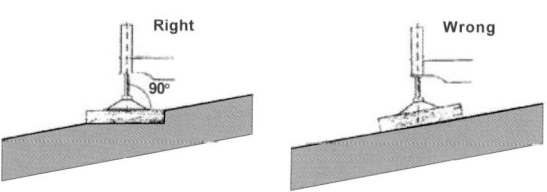

Right | Wrong

 Good quality timber must be used.

Timber and Ply Plate

For small loads this option allows an increase in area to be built up from timbers laid on edge, firmly fixed between two sheets of plywood. This arrangement overcomes the potential instability of loose timbers on edge.

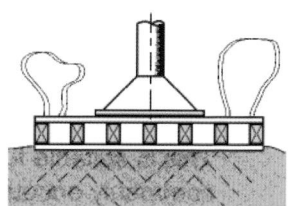

Proprietary Mats

Various proprietary mats are available and may be obtainable from the crane hirer. These should be used strictly in accordance with the mat manufacturer's instructions, noting any limitations.

Steel Grillage

A grillage of steel I-beams (or universal columns). This would normally be used where heavier outrigger loads are involved, or to bridge across obstructions and voids.

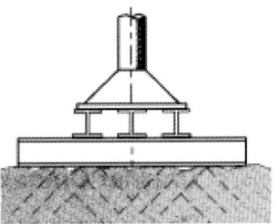

When stacking steel beams, connections between members may be required to avoid instability.

Concrete Pad

For even greater outrigger loading, or on weaker soils, a concrete pad can be used. This can be of mass or reinforced concrete in an excavation or even a precast reinforced pad which is bedded down on sand or similar material.

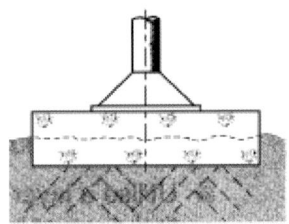

Care must be taken if the pad is to extend above ground level to ensure that the outrigger can be deployed from the chassis of the crane without fouling.

Piled Foundation

For extremely high outrigger loads in extremely weak soil conditions it might be necessary to put down piles into a better strata of soil.

This system is much less flexible and will need more detailed planning. The details of the actual crane are required at an earlier stage and once the piles are installed another make or model of crane, although of similar capacity, may be unsuitable because of varying outrigger dimensions.

Crawler Cranes

Under some ground conditions or site layouts it may be necessary to provide additional hard standings to bring the ground bearing pressures down to an acceptable limit for the crane to travel on or work from.

 Beware of the instability that can occur due to crane vibrations when working on waterlogged beach sand.

Possible methods:

- Utilise a layer of timbers or spreader mats - good quality timber must be used.

- Place a layer of stone, hardcore or crushed concrete (possibly replacing upper layers of weak soil).

- Lay a concrete raft; precast panels might be an economic solution.

- Ground improvement e.g. dynamic compaction, lime stabilisation, stone columns and geotextiles. For these solutions the bearing pressure is defined by on-site testing.

2.6.1   FINAL SITING CHECKS

Even when mats have been correctly dimensioned, care must be exercised so that outriggers or tracks avoid dangerous positions.

The following figures give guidelines for positioning so that stability is not compromised. If a crane operator or lift supervisor find themselves needing to set up within the **"Danger Areas"** further engineering consideration must be given to the problem before moving the crane into these areas.

If you are in a "Danger Area" do not lift with out an engineering assessment being made by a competent engineer.
These areas apply to crawler cranes, lorry mounted telescopic cranes or any other heavy plant.

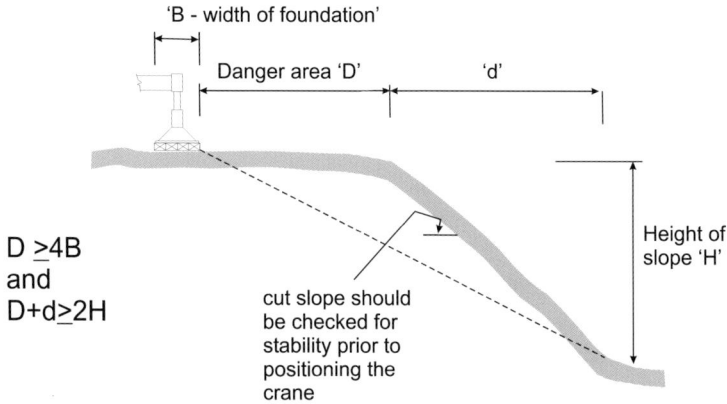

'B - width of foundation'

Danger area 'D'   'd'

D $\geq$ 4B
and
D+d $\geq$ 2H

cut slope should be checked for stability prior to positioning the crane

Height of slope 'H'

A mobile crane was driven too close to the edge of an excavation while attempting to manoeuvre through a narrow gap. The ground gave way and the crane rolled into the excavation.

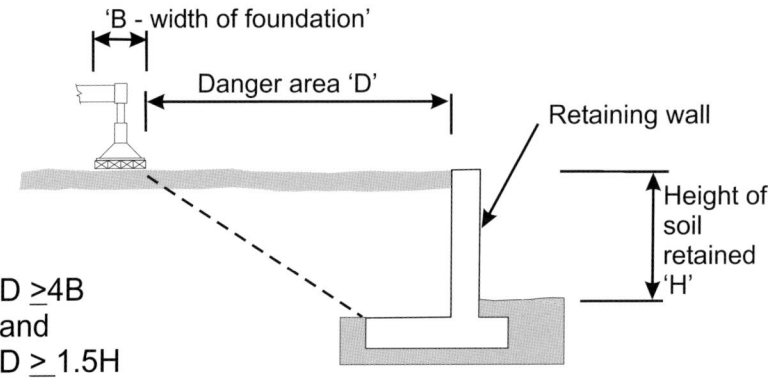

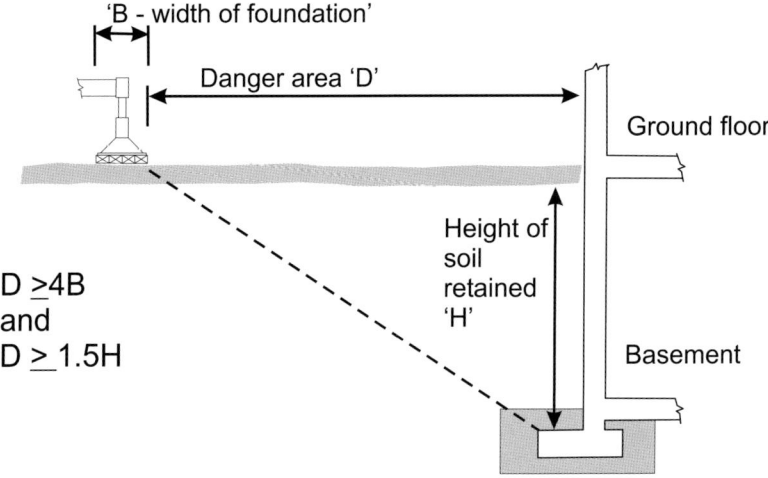

The guidelines given above apply both to work adjacent to permanent structures and to work near to temporary works, eg sheet pile retaining walls, trench support systems, etc.

INTRODUCTION

Many different types of tower crane are available. In the first parts of this Section the most common forms are described and features of their use are given.

The procedures to be followed when siting, erecting and dismantling a crane are also outlined.

Information on base/foundation design is given; this is not exhaustive, but gives an idea of the information required.

Part	Contents
3.1	**Types of Crane**
3.2	Types of Base
3.3	General Considerations
3.4	Ground and Site Conditions
3.5	Loading Cases
3.6	Foundations
3.7	Tying in Cranes

REFERENCE

BS 7121 Part 5: Tower Cranes

3   Tower Cranes

Definition of terms used

The diagram below shows the various components of a tower crane.

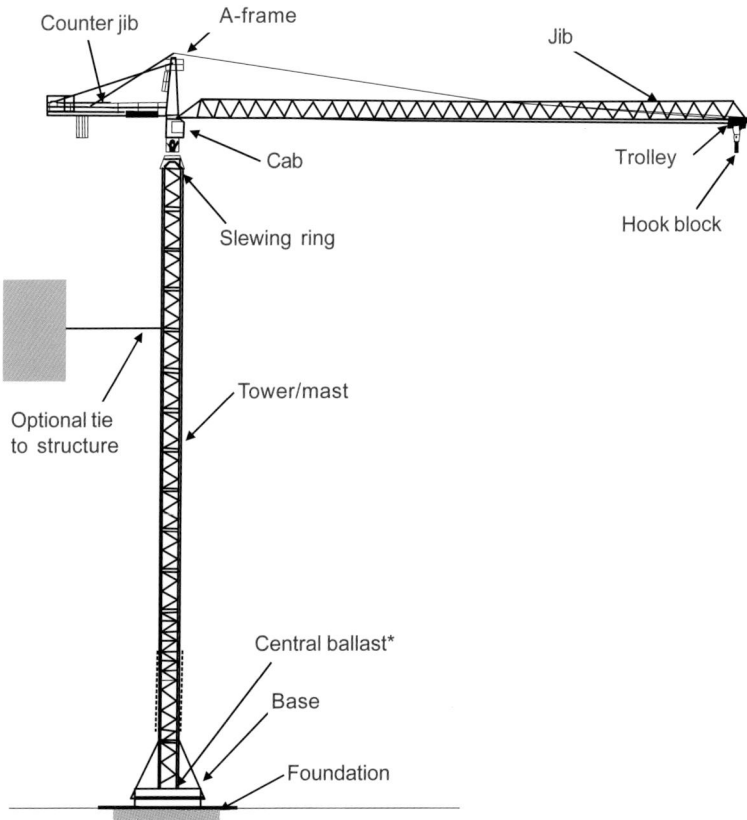

*Not always suppplied by the manufacturer.

> **Note:**
> A tower crane's "metre tonne" rating is a method of sizing it by giving its maximum load x radius value.

3.1.1 TROLLEY JIB (SADDLE JIB)

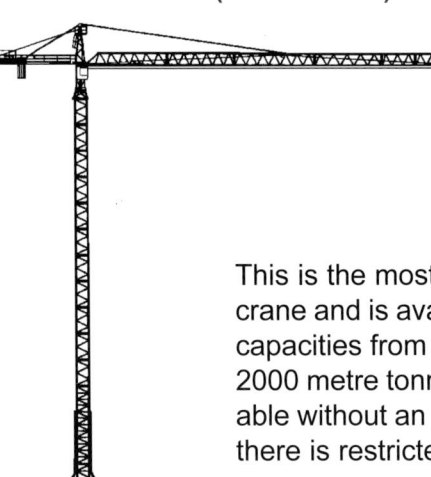

This is the most common type of tower crane and is available in a wide range of capacities from 45 metre tonne to over 2000 metre tonne. Versions are available without an "A" frame, for use when there is restricted headroom.

3.1.2 LUFFING JIB

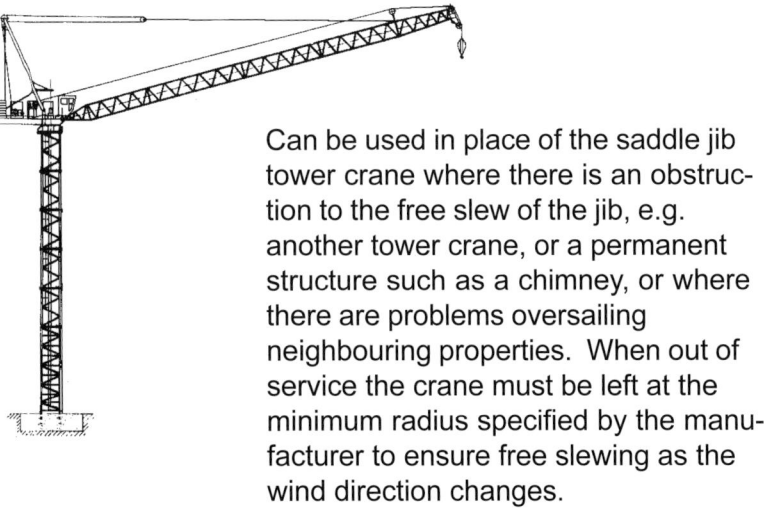

Can be used in place of the saddle jib tower crane where there is an obstruction to the free slew of the jib, e.g. another tower crane, or a permanent structure such as a chimney, or where there are problems oversailing neighbouring properties. When out of service the crane must be left at the minimum radius specified by the manufacturer to ensure free slewing as the wind direction changes.

The range of capacities is 80 metre tonne to 700 metre tonne.

3.1.3 GOOSENECK JIB

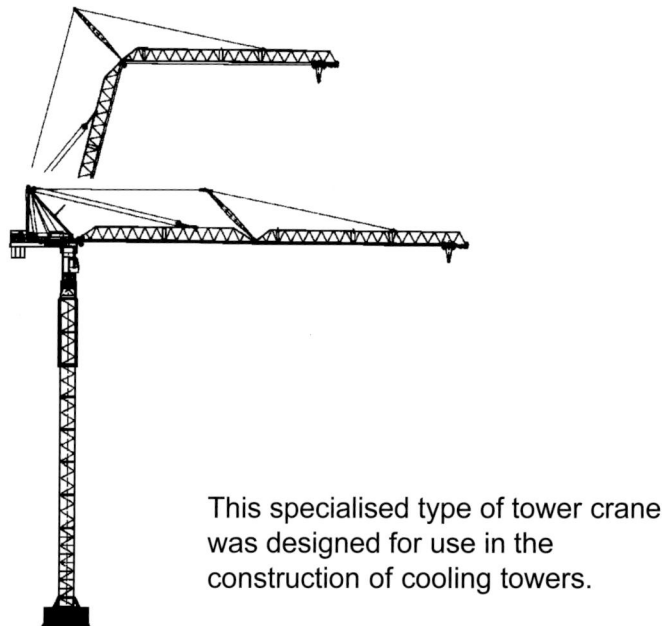

This specialised type of tower crane was designed for use in the construction of cooling towers.

3.1.4 JACK-KNIFE

The jib of this type can be folded up completely when not in operation. It is normally used where there are many tower cranes in close proximity or where there are oversailing problems.

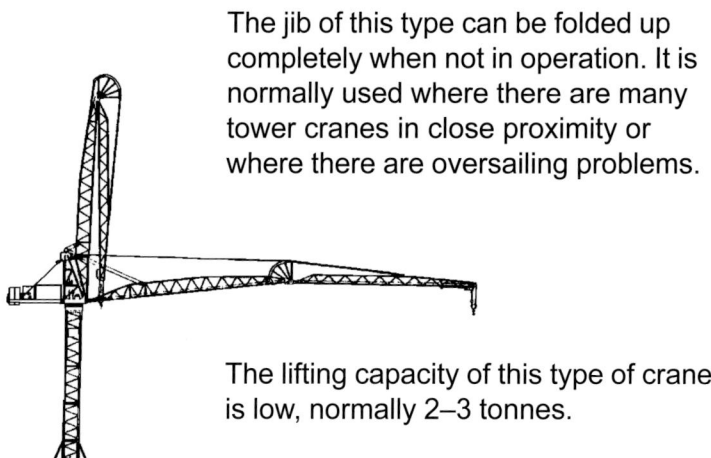

The lifting capacity of this type of crane is low, normally 2–3 tonnes.

3.1.5 FLAT TOP

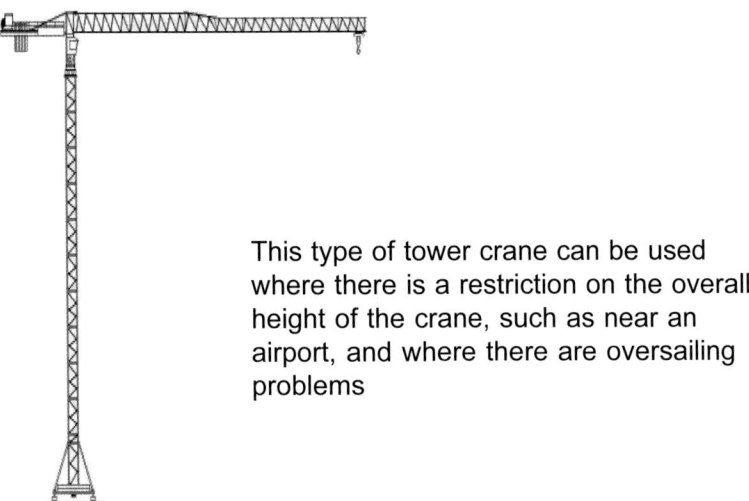

This type of tower crane can be used where there is a restriction on the overall height of the crane, such as near an airport, and where there are oversailing problems

3.1.6 MOBILE SELF ERECTING TOWER CRANE

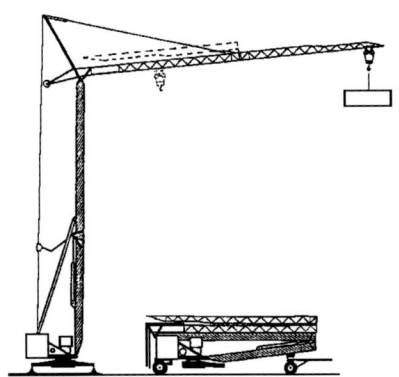

Normally used on smaller projects and for short periods on site where the erection and dismantling costs associated with other types of tower crane cannot be justified.

Capacities generally range from 20 metre tonne to 70 metre tonne.

3.2   Tower Cranes - Types of Base

3.2.1   CAST IN

Often used inside buildings, or if there is
not enough space for a cruciform base or
its outrigger struts. When the crane is
removed, the anchors into the concrete
have to be cut off.

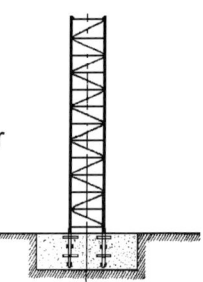

3.2.2   CRUCIFORM

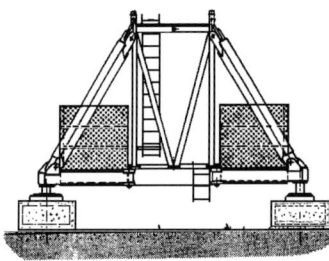

Often used outside buildings, where
there is sufficient space for it to be
assembled. Because the stability of
the crane is usually provided by the
central ballast, the foundation can be
lighter than for a cast-in base.

3.2.3   GRILLAGE

Can be used when a ground bearing
foundation is not practicable. The
steelwork is specially designed for the
particular crane to be used and its
location.

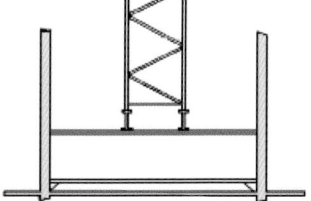

3.2.4   RAIL-MOUNTED

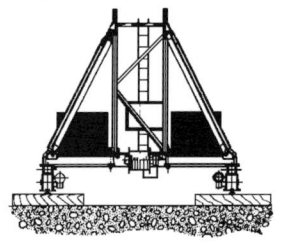

Allows a tower crane to cover a
large area of the site. The track
can be curved if required.

3.2.5 FLOOR CLIMBING

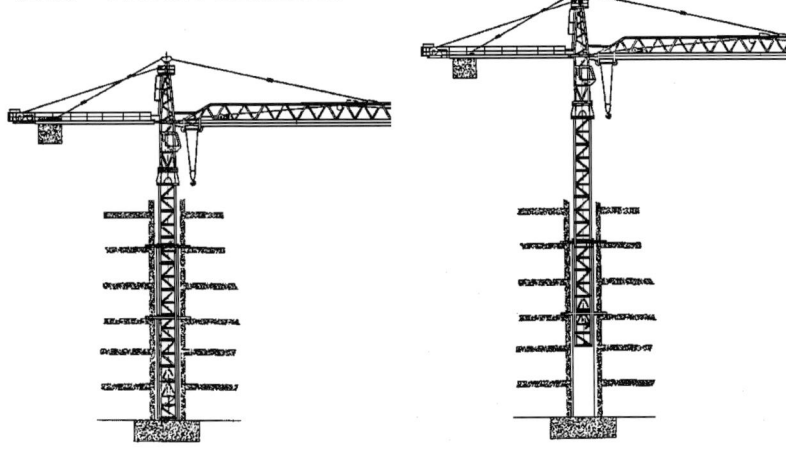

Used when the crane tower is inside a building, often being fitted into a lift shaft.

Other advantages of this system are:

■ No tower in the lower levels of the building, it may be finished earlier.

■ No massive base to take a tall free standing crane.

■ Takes up less room in the building as a tower with a smaller cross section may be used.

3.2.6 CRAWLER UNDERCARRIAGE

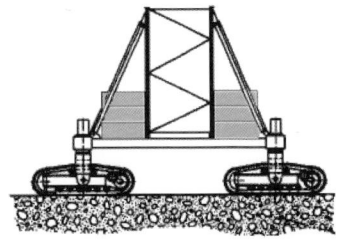

If the tower crane is required to move on site, but rails cannot be installed, then a crawler undercarriage can be used on firm level ground.

3.3 Tower Cranes - General Considerations

3.3.1 SITING

When deciding the location of the tower crane or cranes on site the following need to be considered to ensure stability;

- alterations required during construction (eg increase in tower height);

- construction work which may affect the installed crane (e.g. near base or ties after installation);

- enough room for an adequate foundation to be constructed;

- effect of wind (especially out of service);

- vaults or underground services;

- maximum load, lifting radius and hook height requirements.

In addition the following should also be considered;

- proximity hazards including overhead cables, structures, railways, flight paths and other cranes;

- access for erection and dismantling, and room for pre-assembly of the jib on the ground;

- availability of adequate electrical supply;

- restrictions on oversailing neighbouring properties (Airspace rights).

A tower crane was being erected on a site and had the counter jib and counter ballast attached, but not the main jib. The counter jib and cab were being slewed before attaching the jib, when the crane overturned. Subsequent investigation revealed that too much counter ballast had been installed because the erection supervisor had left his spectacles at home and could not consult the erection manual.

3.3.2 ERECTION

Before erection can take place, the following checks on the foundation for the tower crane need to be completed.

- Have the design and drawings of the foundation been checked by a suitably qualified engineer for adequacy in concept and detail?

- Has the foundation been constructed in accordance with the drawings?

- Have any permanent works used as part of the foundation been analysed by the Temporary Works Designer and/or passed to the Permanent Works Designer for approval?

- Have any ties been fabricated and installed?

- Have any restrictions imposed by the Temporary or Permanent Works Designer been taken into account?

The tower crane should be assembled following the manufacturer's instructions and using a safe system of work (BS 7121: Part 5: Section 11). Therefore, a site specific method statement should be produced prior to the crane being erected. All personnel involved should follow the method statement.

REFERENCES		
Health and Safety at Work etc Act	-	information, instruction, training
Management of Health and Safety at Work Regulations 1999	-	risk assessment
Construction (Design and Management) Regulations 1994	-	risk assessment

3.3.3   DISMANTLING

The tower crane must be dismantled following the manufacturer's instructions and a site specific method statement. Central ballast, if used, must be sufficient for the crane to remain stable whilst partially dismantled, especially if left overnight.

 Note that the dismantling operation should be allowed for in the initial planning stage.

3.3.4   USE

For safe use of a tower crane the personnel involved in the operation should be trained to a suitable level.This includes the Appointed Person, crane coordinator, driver, slingers, signallers and maintenance personnel (requirements are given in BS 7121: Part 5: Section 7)

During use, the following points must be adhered to.

- The safe working load (SWL) of the crane must not be exceeded.

- Prior to lifting, the hoist rope must be plumb, and the load free to lift (not snagged).

- The load must not be dragged along the ground.

- The load must be correctly slung, as jerking or sudden loss of the load can affect crane stability.

- The manufacturer's maximum stated wind speed must not be exceeded.

- The crane must not be used when the speed of the wind exceeds that at which the load can be safely handled and lifted.

- Periodic checks should be made on the crane structure on a daily and weekly basis (BS 7121 Part 2 Section 6).

Tower cranes must not be used for grabbing, demolition balling, piling or multiple lifting.

REFERENCES
BS 7121: Parts 1, 2 and 5

3.4.1   SITE DATA

The following information will be required for the design of a foundation for a tower crane;

■ location of site and description of surroundings;

■ soil data, including allowable bearing pressure (or capacity of piles). Any variation in the soil conditions around the position and level of the foundation should be noted;

■ details of obstructions (eg services, piles, pile caps, foundations) and of any other limitations on the shape and size of the foundation;

■ details, including reinforcement, of ground-bearing slab or other structural members, if these are to be utilised;

■ position and details of adjacent structures on which load could be imposed by the crane foundation (eg retaining walls).

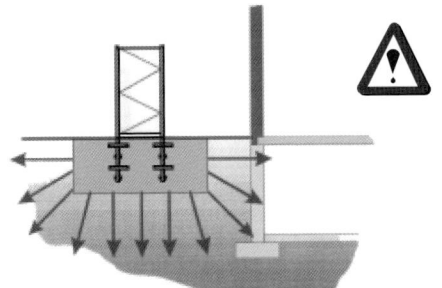 Where information is unavailable, a site investigation must be carried out (see Section 1.5).

3.5   Tower Cranes - Loading Cases

3.5.1   LOADING CASES

When designing the support for a crane it is necessary to take account of the most severe static and dynamic loading conditions possible, as influenced by such factors as the weight of the crane (including any counterweight), the weight being lifted (including lifting gear), overturning moments, slewing torque, horizontal forces, dynamic forces, wind loading, ice loading, etc. It is necessary to consider both the in-service and out-of-service conditions since the most critical loading case may be associated with erection or dismantling of the crane or with high wind loading etc, and not with any lifting operation.

Manufacturers of tower cranes supply specifications which include computed values for the vertical and horizontal forces and overturning moments transmitted to the foundation for both the in-service and out-of-service conditions.

In very exposed areas (eg cliff tops) it may be necessary to allow for out-of-service wind speeds higher than the manufacturer's normal loading.

 Before signboards or decorations are fitted to a tower crane, the manufacturer's agreement should be obtained. The additional weight and wind loading area need to be taken into account when assessing the support arrangements.

3.5.2   CAST IN BASES

For cast in bases on both pad and piled foundations, the horizontal loading (H) is due to wind and dynamic effects. The vertical loading (V) is due to the weight of the crane and load.

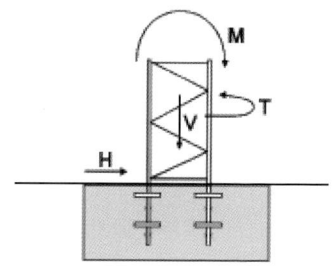

Cast in base on pad foundation

The overturning moment (M) is due to wind, movement and the crane being out of balance. The slewing moment (T) is due to the crane slewing in operation and the effect of side wind on the jib. Stability of the crane against overturning is provided by the foundation. These forces are also used in the design of grillage bases and for floor-climbing cranes.

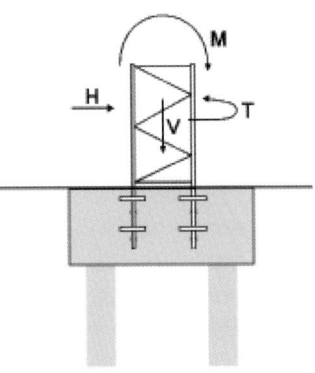

Cast in base on piled foundation

3.5.3 RAIL-MOUNTED AND CRUCIFORM BASES

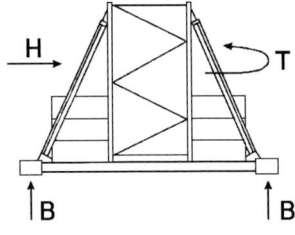

The horizontal loading (H) is due to wind and movement of the crane. The vertical bogie/corner loading (B) is due to all forces acting on the crane, both static and dynamic. The slewing moment (T) is due to the crane slewing in operation. For these bases, stability is usually provided by the central ballast mounted on the crane structure itself. Therefore it is usually unnecessary to consider the foundation's stability against overturning. These forces will also apply to crawler-based cranes.

3.5.4 IN SERVICE

The in-service condition occurs when the crane is handling loads up to the safe working load in permissible wind speeds and other conditions as specified by the manufacturer.

3.5   Tower Cranes - Loading Cases

3.5.5   OUT OF SERVICE

The Out-of-service condition occurs when the crane is either not required for use, or out of use, without a load on the lifting attachment and in conditions as specified by the manufacturer. This condition will generally include a higher wind speed than that permitted for the in-service conditions and includes those forces produced by the most unfavourable conditions from either erection or wind. It will not include slewing moment (T) as the crane must be allowed to slew freely in the wind.

Rail mounted cranes will normally be clamped to the rails to stop them travelling in high winds.

3.5.6   ERECTION, TESTING AND DISMANTLING

The forces imposed during erection, testing or dismantling are generally less than the out-of-service forces. However, the manufacturer's data should be checked for each case.

3.5.7   MANUFACTURER'S DATA

The information from the manufacturer will vary depending on the make and the type of crane involved and will include both in-service and out-of-service conditions. Most manufacturers will supply un-factored data i.e. the forces given will be the actual forces acting at the base of the crane.

For static cranes some manufacturer's data for overturning moments includes sets of figures for wind both square and diagonal to the mast. When only one set of figures is given, it is for the worst case and the same value should be used for both directions.

For rail-mounted and cruciform-based cranes all forces acting on the crane structure, i.e. dead weight, working load, wind load, inertia forces, and ballast required for stability, will have been taken into account in the calculation of the vertical bogie/corner forces quoted by the manufacturer.

3.6.1 FOUNDATION DESIGN

While there are a number of standards, both national and international, which lay down requirements for the design and use of tower crane superstructures, little attention has been paid to the foundations. No standard appears to set down criteria for the design of crane foundations. Building foundation standards do not cover the high overturning moments and dynamic forces occurring in tower crane foundations.

For this reason foundation design for tower cranes should be referred to designers with specific expertise in this type of design.

 The design of tower crane foundations requires close consultation between a number of parties such as the crane manufacturer, Temporary Works Designer, Permanent Works Designer and Structural Engineer.

Details of suitable forms for the recording of the certification of foundation design and design checking are given in Section 5.2.

3.6.2 CAST IN

In this case the tower crane is anchored to a large concrete block, which may be incorporated into the foundations of the building or be supported on piles. The foundation must have sufficient mass and base area to carry the vertical and horizontal forces and the overturning moments into the ground without any possibility of overturning, without causing excessive settlement, and without exceeding the allowable ground bearing pressure. Horizontal forces are normally resisted by friction under the foundation and/or passive resistance on the side of the foundation. It is important that the foundation remains level; tower cranes are designed to have their bases level to approximately 1 in 500 at all times.

3.6   Tower Cranes - Foundations

3.6.3   CRUCIFORM

When the crane is mounted on a cruciform base, the four corner plates will usually be founded on four concrete pads, four piles or a large concrete slab. The size of the foundation has to be calculated from the magnitude of the corner forces and the allowable ground bearing pressure, taking note of the maximum allowable variations in deflection/settlement between the four corners of the base.

3.6.4   GRILLAGE

The loadings that occur with this type of base will be specific to the grillage being used, and will be calculated along with the design for the grillage itself. Normally the limiting factor for the forces is the capacity of the permanent works to which the grillage is attached.
These will be established by the Structural Engineer.

3.6.5   FLOOR CLIMBING

When building a tall structure, the cost of the tower for a tower crane extending from foundation level to the top of the building can be very high. As an alternative the crane and its tower may be climbed up the structure as construction progresses, using the completed part of the structure to take all the forces generated by the crane. Climbing is achieved by using a hydraulic climbing section at the bottom of the tower to push the crane up to the next level. The base of the tower takes the vertical forces and part of the overturning moment whilst a tie higher up the mast takes the horizontal forces of the remainder of the moment.

The crane will generally start from foundation level on a correctly designed cast-in foundation. Once climbing has started the subsequent supports will be the permanent works and these require the approval of the Permanent Works Designer.

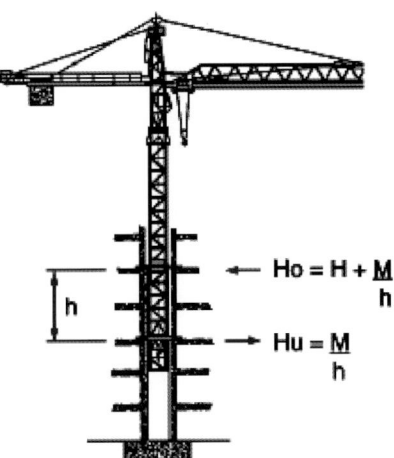

Here, M, H and V are the Overturning Moment and Horizontal and Vertical forces supplied by the manufacturer for a tower height equal to that above the top tie. The slewing moment is also taken by the top tie.

$$H_o = H + \frac{M}{h}$$

$$H_u = \frac{M}{h}$$

3.6.6   RAIL-MOUNTED

Travelling bases generally run on standard railway type rails, but the local forces from tower cranes are high. While a locomotive may weigh around 120 tonnes, its weight is spread fairly evenly over 10 to 12 wheels. A tower crane, on the other hand, can put this same force onto just two wheels only 600mm to 800mm apart! Foundations for tower crane track, therefore, may need to be far more substantial than the typical sleepers-on-ballast arrangement that a railway uses. A further limitation is that a tower crane is very sensitive to differential deflections of its bogies, e.g. a bogie with 100 tonnes on it may only be permitted to deflect 6mm more than one with no load on it.

There are several types of track construction available, with different foundation requirements. Some examples are illustrated overleaf.

 Depending on the foundation provided for the rails, it may be necessary to inspect the track weekly to ensure that deflection limits (provided by the manufacturer) are not exceeded.

3.6 Tower Cranes - Foundations

A. Rails on Timber Bearers

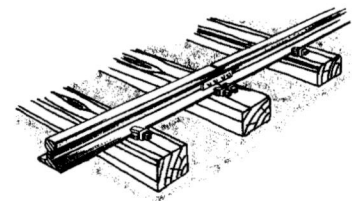

Timber bearers used are frequently 300mm x 300mm x 2400mm long, spaced along the rail at 600mm centres. The force on each sleeper may be taken to be as the sketches below.

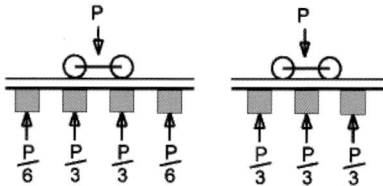

B. Rails on Concrete Beams or Slabs

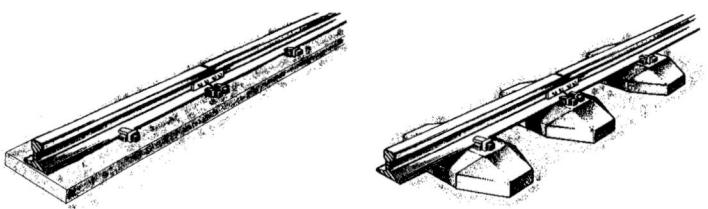

Rail on Concrete Beam   Rail on Concrete Blocks

The usual method of fixing the rails to the concrete is by drilling and bolting using suitable expansion bolts or chemical anchors and clips. The centres of the reinforcement links should be the same as the bolt centres to avoid clashing. The beam may be designed either as a beam on elastic foundations, or as a series of pads, each of which is the width of the beam and has a length less than the bogie centres. The width and depth of the beam should be sufficient to accommodate the bolt.

3.7.1   TYING IN CRANES

Sometimes, due to the limitations of the tower crane or its foundation, it is necessary to tie a tower crane some way up its tower to another structure to achieve sufficient height to complete the project under construction. The tie involves a collar being clamped round the tower, which is then connected to the supporting structure. The following diagram shows the forces involved.

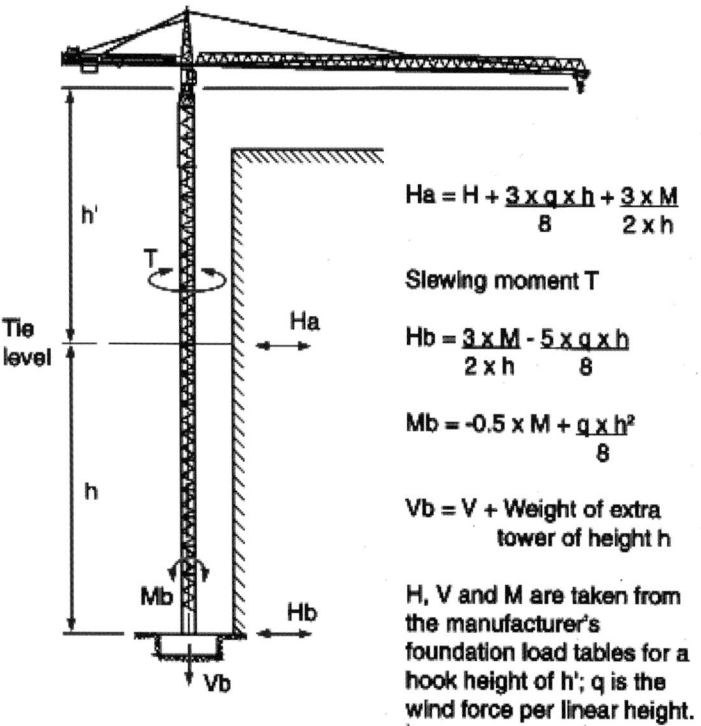

$$Ha = H + \frac{3 \times q \times h}{8} + \frac{3 \times M}{2 \times h}$$

Slewing moment T

$$Hb = \frac{3 \times M}{2 \times h} - \frac{5 \times q \times h}{8}$$

$$Mb = -0.5 \times M + \frac{q \times h^2}{8}$$

$Vb = V +$ Weight of extra tower of height h

H, V and M are taken from the manufacturer's foundation load tables for a hook height of h'; q is the wind force per linear height.

 Most tower sections can only be connected to a tie at certain points

 Consult the Manufacturer for the maximum allowable shear forces (Ha) on the tower. They may be in the order of 300kN.

INTRODUCTION

The previous sections of this guide have dealt with the most commonly used cranes and their usual applications on site.

However, there are some other specialist applications which may be encountered and there are also other types of equipment that may be classified as cranes.

4.1 Special Cases - Special Applications

4.1.1 MULTIPLE LIFTS -

Lifting one load with more than one crane

This is an extremely complex operation and needs a great deal of planning. Due to the possibility of overloading one or the other of the cranes, the S.W.L. of each crane may need to be reduced by 20% or more. This helps to take into account any tendency for ropes to be slightly out of vertical, or any dynamic loadings.

The following points should be remembered:

- Cranes should be of similar capacities and performance.
- All movement should be as slow as possible, with no sudden motions.
- Slew, derrick and hoist speeds of cranes should match.
- The centre of gravity of the load should be calculated so that the lifting points can be chosen correctly.
- Good communications are imperative, with one responsible person in charge.

 Tower cranes should not be used for multiple lifting.

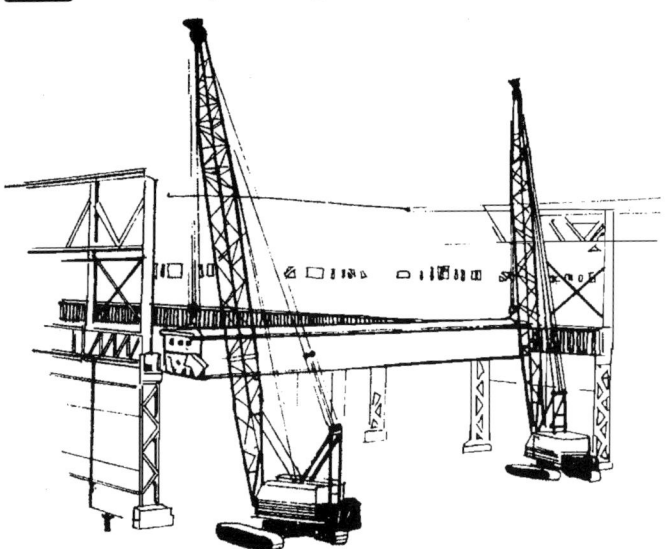

The use of remote reading inclinometers to monitor the level of the load should be considered during multiple lifting operations.

REFERENCE

BS 7121: Parts 1 and 3

4.1.2 RINGERS

This arrangement converts a crawler crane into a static installation and allows its lifting capacity to be increased significantly. However the ground preparation required is much more onerous as the ring attachment has to be supported around its complete circumference.

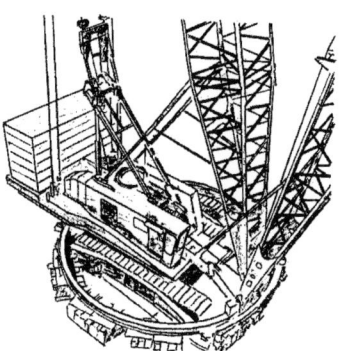

4.1.3 SUPERLIFT/MAXILIFT

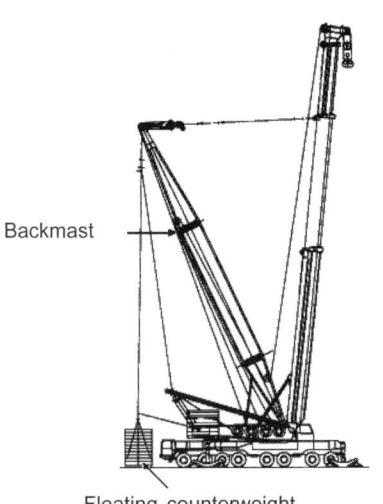

Backmast

Floating counterweight

By adding a backmast and additional "floating" counterweight to some mobile/crawler cranes, their capacities can be greatly enhanced, particularly at large working radii. Although this equipment is "mobile", assembly and disassembly (involving assistance from smaller service cranes) takes longer than a standard crane. Additional consideration has to be given to the positioning of, and loadings under, the "floating" counterweight.

4.2 Special Cases - Other Lifting Appliances

4.2.1 PORTAL CRANES

Portal cranes may be encountered on site especially where a great deal of on-site preassembly and prefabrication is undertaken.

There are two main types:

Rail-mounted

Often used for on-site reinforcement yards or precast areas.

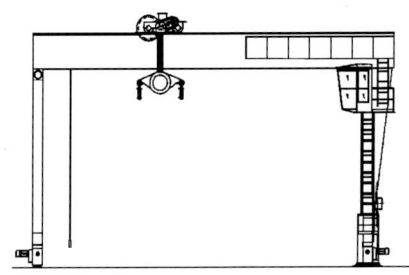

Rubber-tyred

Used for moving large precast elements around site.

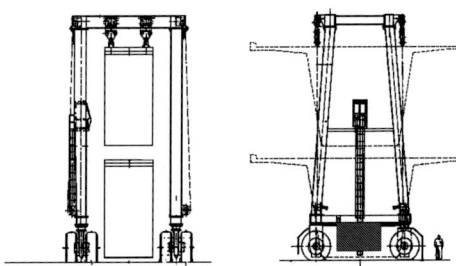

 All types of portal cranes need firm level ground on which to operate.

4.2.2 YARD CRANES

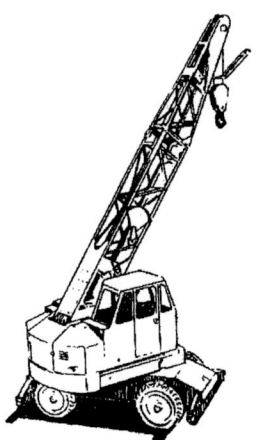

These cranes are primarily intended for operation in industrial locations where working surfaces are significantly better than most construction sites, and are generally designed for Pick-and-Carry operations.

Their characteristics are basically identical to those of telescopic mobiles.

These machines should always be operated in accordance with the manufacturer's instructions.

 Yard cranes can only operate safely on firm, level, surfaced areas.

4.2.3 TELESCOPIC HANDLERS

These industrial trucks are an increasingly used tool on construction sites.

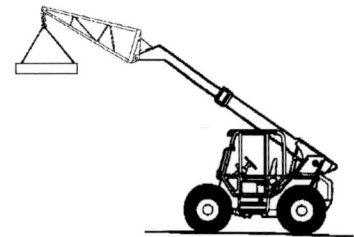

The basic stability principles previously described apply to these machines and careful planning for their use and training of operators is required to ensure accidents do not occur.

 When used for lifting, the correct manufacturer's attachment must be used, and lifting operations carried out in accordance with the requirements of LOLER and BS 7121

4.2.4   EXCAVATORS USED AS CRANES

Excavators are often used as cranes for such operations as lifting pipes during drainage and sewer work.

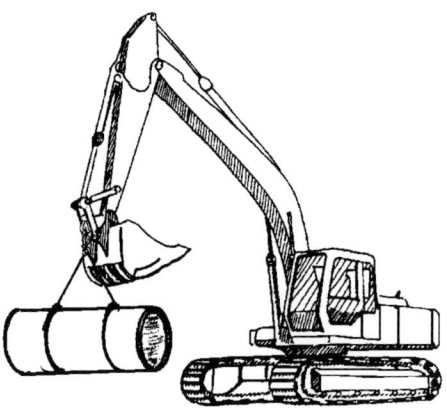

Should an excavator be used to lift materials, other than excavated material or fill, then by definition it becomes a crane and the lifting operations carried out in accordance with the requirements of LOLER and BS 7121.

INTRODUCTION

As stressed previously, all lifting operations must be thoroughly planned to ensure successful, safe and economic solutions. With so many factors, in varying permutations, having to be considered during the planning stage, and checked before and during the execution stage, the use of pre-determined check lists and standardised documentation is strongly recommended.

These may relate to the planning process itself, the people, the environment and the equipment. There are associated statutory requirements for certain documents.

This section of the handbook provides typical checklists for various elements. These may be used as an *aide memoir*, as a basis for similar checklists for other elements or indeed for more detailed checklists.

Part	Contents
5.1	**Checklists**
5.2	**Sample Documents**

 Documentation is a "means to an end" and not an end in itself. It must therefore be used only by those who have a thorough understanding of its purpose and its limitations.

5.1   Checklists

5.1.1   Key Elements of a Safe System of Work
(See section 1 and BS 7121: Part 1 and 3)

Key elements of a safe system of work for lifting operations include the following :

- Planning the operation (including risk assessment(s))
- Provision of properly trained, competent personnel.
- Selection, provision and use of suitable crane and equipment.
- Adequate supervision by properly trained, competent personnel having the necessary authority to control the operation.
- Ensuring that all necessary test certificates and other documents are in order.
- Preventing any unauthorised movement or use.
- Ensuring the safety of persons not involved in the lifting operations.

5.1.2   The Load and the Lift
(See section 1,2 and 3)

- Maximum weight of load (plus lifting gear)
- Maximum height of lift
- Maximum radius of lift
- Centre of gravity of load
- Containment of loose materials
- Any lifting points, (location and adequacy)
- Wind area presented by load
- Structural stability/integrity/rigidity of load whilst suspended
- Need for special lifting beams or frames

5.1.3 The Location
(See sections 1,2 and 3)

Crane access - height, width, swept path, weight restrictions	☐
Room for crane rigging	☐
Level approach and working areas	☐
Ground bearing capacity	☐
Voids, traps, underground services, adjacent excavations etc	☐
Obstructions to lifting (overhead cables, existing buildings, other cranes etc.)	☐
Exclusion zones	☐
Road closure	☐
Rail possession	☐
Public interface	☐
Wind (means of monitoring and action levels)	☐

5.1.4 The Specifying Team
(See section 1)

The Appointed Person	☐
Will the crane be hired and managed on site or will the lift be fully subcontracted?	☐
The crane specifier	☐
The foundation specifier	☐
The lifting gear specifier	☐

5.1   Checklists

5.1.5   The Crane
(see Sections 2,3 and 4)

Crane provider and technical representative	
Crane make, model and rig configuration	
Outrigger loads/Foundation loads	
Erection and dismantling procedures	
Special ballast	
Site testing	

Certification

Test of automatic safe load indicators - before erection and when first taken into use	
Thorough examination and test - 4-yearly	
Thorough examination - 12-monthly (or 6-monthly if to be used for lifting persons).*	
Inspection of crane and automatic safe load indicators - weekly	
Test and examination of anchorages and/or ballasting - before erection and first taking into use	

* As an alternative LOLER allows thorough examination under an "examination scheme". Details of this approach are given in Regulation 9 of LOLER and clause 7 of BS 7121-2:2003. Examination schemes are not recommended for cranes used on construction sites, due to the wide variations in operating and environmental conditions across the industry.

5.1.6   The Lifting Gear

List all items (e.g. chain/wire rope/fibre slings, shackles, spreader beams, swivels, eyebolts)	
S.W.L. of each item	
Marking of each item	
Compatibility of each item	
Lengths of slings/beams (to suit size and shape of load and method of slinging)	
Distribution of load in each leg of multi-leg sling	
Angle between sling legs (should be less then 90°)	

Certification :

Test and examination - before first use and after alteration/repair	☐
Thorough examination - 6-monthly	☐
Method of attachment/slinging	☐
Arrangements for storage, issue and inspection of lifting gear	☐

5.1.7 The Temporary Works
(see Sections 1, 2 and 3)

Crane base and outrigger support :

Special design (by whom ?)	☐
Checked for compliance (by whom ?)	☐
Standard solution - (specify which)	☐

5.1.8 The Operating Team
(see Section 1)

The competence of each of the following to be checked:

The Appointed Person	☐
The crane driver (operator)	☐
The slinger/signaller (s)	☐

5.1 Checklists

5.1.9 INSPECTION OF TOWER CRANE FOUNDATIONS
(See section 3)

The precise scope, frequency and responsibility for inspection must be clearly specified for the particular foundation arrangement chosen.

Pre-erection inspections may include :

All foundations	-	details in accordance with foundation designer's drawings and details
Reinforced concrete	-	concrete of correct grade and sufficient maturity
Piles	-	results of pile tests
	-	sufficient reinforcement bond length into pile cap
Steelwork	-	steel correct grade
	-	bolts tight (check if particular torque required)
	-	weld quality
Cast-in items	-	level, plumb and tolerance (foundation anchors, ties etc)
Rail track	-	bedding properly compacted
	-	track centres and level to correct tolerance
	-	limit ramps and end stops correctly positioned and firmly fixed
	-	rails earthed
	-	exclusion zone (fencing)

Ongoing monitoring may include :

All foundations	-	level checks
Reinforced concrete	-	inspection for cracking, especially around cast-in items.
Steelwork (including ties)	-	bolts tight
	-	inspection for cracks in welds
Rail track	-	rail centres and level
	-	limit ramps and end stops correctly positioned and firmly fixed.

Records of all such inspections, monitoring and any resulting remedial actions should be maintained on site.

5.1.10 METHOD STATEMENTS FOR TOWER CRANE ERECTION AND DISMANTLING

(See section 3)

Method statements for erection and dismantling of cranes should include :

i) Arrangements for the management of the erection/dismantling including co-ordination with site and the responsibilities and authority of supervisory personnel at all levels. ☐

ii) Erection/Dismantling sequences. ☐

iii) The detailed method of erecting/dismantling the crane. The erection scheme should be devised so that activities such as slinging, lifting, unslinging, initial connection, alignment and final connecting can be carried out safety. (The scheme may be detailed by reference to the appropriate sections of the manufacturer's manual). ☐

iv) Provisions to aid the prevention of falls from height including safe means of access and safe places of work. ☐

v) Protection from falls of materials, tools and debris. ☐

vi) The provision of suitable cranage to assist in the operations including arrangements for access, adequate siting and outrigger foundations. ☐

vii) The provision of tools and equipment of sufficient strength and quality. ☐

viii) Contingency arrangements should there be, for instance, high wind, a breakdown of plant or components delivered out of sequence. ☐

ix) Arrangements for delivery, stocking, storing and movement of components on site. ☐

x) Details of site features, layout and access, with notes on how these may affect proposed arrangements and methods of working. ☐

xi) Arrangements for examination and testing following erection (including testing of electrics and lightning protection). ☐

xii) Provision of Personal Protective Equipment. ☐

xiii) COSHH assessments for lubricants. ☐

5.1   Checklists

Method statements for the climbing of tower cranes using an external climbing frame should include:

i)   Arrangements for transportation of the climbing frame to site, safe off loading and checking for damage in transit before assembly on the tower.

ii)   Arrangements for briefing of the climbing team and allocation of specific duties to each member, before starting operations on site.

iii)   Establishment of a suitable exclusion zone to protect others.

iv)   Arrangements for safe assembly of the frame around the crane mast to avoid collapse or dislodgement of any part.

v)   Positive inspection of the assembled parts of the climbing frame by a competent person to check on safety critical features such as the tightness of bolts, the correct location of the guide rollers or wheels and the absence of damage.

vi)   Positioning of mast sections to be added to the tower on the ground so as to avoid or minimize the need to slew the crane between climbs.

vii)   Arrangements for obtaining site-specific weather forecasts at relevant heights and for measuring real-time wind speed and direction.

viii)   Responsibilities for monitoring other safety critical parameters including crane jib alignment, actual jib radius and permitted free height of the crane.

ix)   Arrangements to prevent deliberate or inadvertent slewing during climbing e.g. by ensuring that any interlock for the power supply is in sound condition, the slew brake is correctly engaged and any positive scotch or other device to prevent inadvertent slewing is in place.

x) Checks on the positive engagement of the hydraulic climbing cylinder assembly on the mast (pins and lugs or support shoes) and the means of preventing disengagement during climbing.

xi) Checks to ensure that moveable parts have been secured before a climb, eg any temporary support beam or a trolley which allows the hydraulic ram assembly to be moved clear of the mast during setting up.

xii) Arrangements for providing a suitable balance weight (where indicated in the climbing instructions).

xiii) Procedure for balancing the crane, giving permitted tolerances from the balancing radius specified in the operating instructions and other parameters such as wind speed.

xiv) Temporary fixing of mast sections and permitted arrangements for overcoming fit problems to move new mast sections into position.

xv) Contingency arrangements for dealing with events such as wind speed increasing above the manufacturer's maximum for climbing, the crane going out of balance, or breakdown of the climbing system power pack, and for leaving the crane and climbing frame in a safe condition.

xvi) Safe dismantling of the frame.

5.2 Sample Documents

5.2.1   TOWER CRANE FOUNDATION DESIGN CERTIFiCATE

Certificate N°.......

TOWER CRANE FOUNDATION DESIGN CERTIFICATE

Project:.....................   **Tower crane N°/Location**.....................

Tower Crane Type................................

Design criteria and references: (Loading data, specifications, contract drawings, British Standards, standard data etc)

Drawings and Documents issued to site:

Limitations or Restricions: (if the foundation design relies on the use of the permanent works, lhe designer should state whether or not the permanent works has been analysed).

We certify that reasonable professional skill and care has been used in the preparation of this design, that the details have been checked for compliance with the relevant standards listed above and that the design has been accurately translated into the drawings and other documents issued to site:

Signed .... **Date** ....

Name   ....

Position..

Company..

5.2.2   TOWER CRANE FOUNDATION DESIGN CHECK CERTIFICATE

Certificate N° ....

TOWER CRANE FOUNDATION DESIGN CHECK CERTIFICATE

Project: ....Tower Crane N°/Location ....

Tower Crane Type ....

Information Checked: (Drawing Nos/document references)

Design Criteria: (Loading data, British Standard Specifications, etc)

Notes and observations:

We certify that reasonable professional skill and care has been used in checking the design of this tower crane foundation including the drawings and other documents listed above:

Signed .... Date ....

Name ....

Position ....

Company ....

5.2   Sample Documents

5.2.3   TOWER CRANE FOUNDATION PRE-ERECTION INSPECTION CERTIFICATE

Certificate N° ....

TOWER CRANE FOUNDATION
PRE-ERECTION INSPECTION CERTIFICATE

Project: ....   **Tower Crane N°/Location** ....

Tower Crane Type ....

Item (delete where not applicable)	Checked by	Date
Compliance with design drawings/specification		
Level check		
Cast-in items within tolerance		
Concrete quality/strength		
Pile tests		
Steel grade		
Weld quality		
Bolts - grade, torque, tightness		
Track rails - levels, spacing, fixings, end stops, limit switch ramps, earthing		

Documents against which foundation has been checked:
(Drawings Nos/ Document Reference)

Foundation Design Cert No........

Design Check Cert No ....

The above inspections having been carried out satisfactorily, erection of the tower crane superstructure may proceed:

Notes and observations:

Signed.................... **Date**..............

Name ....

Position ....

Company ....

Appendices

Part	Contents
A1	**Mobile Crane Spreader: Typical calculation**
A2	**Accident Case Studies**

INTRODUCTION

1. The calculation which follows is a typical simple calculation for a timber mat under the outrigger of a mobile crane. It is intended to amplify the text within the body of this guide, see sections 2.4 and 2.5.

    It is an example, to show the kind of calculations that must be carried out, both for the area of mat required to achieve an acceptable ground pressure, and for the strength of the mat required to spread the load over that area.

> **It is not a standard calculation suitable for all cases. Different situations will require differing calculations.**

2. Only carry out calculations yourself if you are competent to do so; otherwise get a competent person to do them.

3. Calculations should be checked independently; we can all make mistakes.

Mobile Crane Spreaders - Typical Calculation A1

PROPERTIES OF TIMBER SLEEPERS:

Normal size	10" x 5"
Actual size	248 x 123mm approximately

$$Z = \frac{bd^2}{6} = \frac{248 \times 123^2}{6} = 625 \times 10^3 \text{ mm}^3$$

Permissible Stresses derived from BS 5268 and BS5975:

Assumptions: timber strength class SC5

dry exposure (sleepers have normally been treated with creosote or similar which will tend to repel moisture) short duration loading (equivalent to "dead + imposed + snow + 15 second wind gust" in BS 5268)

STRESSES IN N/mm²

	Bending (f)	Shear (q)	Bearing
BS 5268			
Grade Stress	10.0	1.0	2.8
K_3 - Duration	1.5	1.5	1.5
K_7 - Depth	1.10	-	-
BS 5975			
Temporary Works	-	1.5	1.2
Permissable Stress	16.5	2.25	5.0

Therefore Moment of Resistance $= fZ = 16.5 \times 625 \times 10^3 \times 10^{-6} = 10.3 \text{ KNm}$

Permissible shear force $= \dfrac{qA}{1.5} = \dfrac{2.25 \times 248 \times 123 \times 10^{-3}}{1.5} = 45.7 \text{ KN}$

Notes:
a) BS 5975 has not been used alone, because it only gives wet stresses.
b) Table 9 in BS 5268 has been used for the grade stresses because of difficulty in interpreting BS EN 338, which specifies characteristic strengths (not permissible stresses or partial factors of safety).

SLEEPER MAT FOR MOBILE CRANE OUTRIGGER

DATA:

Crane: 30 tonne capacity truck-mounted mobile.
Size of outrigger pads : 400 x 400 mm.

Maximum outrigger load: take 33 tonnes   **1**
       - i.e. approx 330 kN

Ground : dense to very dense sandy gravel.

REQUIRED SIZE OF MAT :

Using factor of safety = 2 ,
    and $\phi = 40°$,
area of mat required $\doteq \underline{0.9 \, m^2}$

For granular soil, this area can be square
or rectangular ; try 3 no. sleepers wide
x 1200 mm long
   i.e.   750 mm x 1200 mm   **2**
   i.e. area = $0.75 × 1.2 = 0.9 \, m^2$
          ———————

1 The maximum load has been taken from the table of typical cranes on page 47 of this guide. In practice, it is better to obtain the outrigger loads from the crane manufacturer, via the hirer, for the actual crane and jib configuration to be used.

2 The size of mat has been derived from the graph on page 49 of this guide, reproduced opposite.

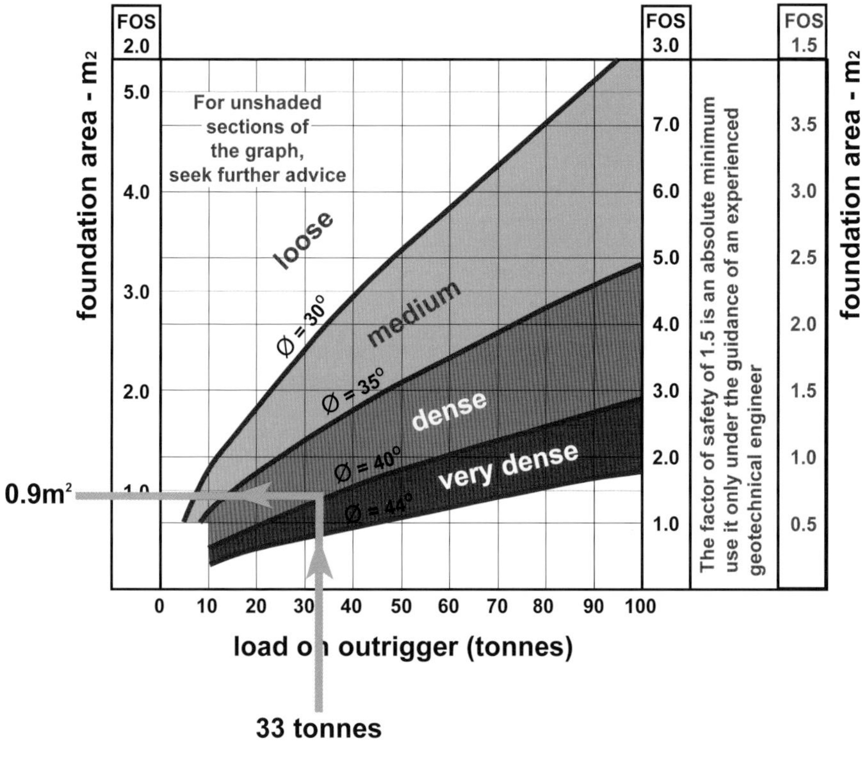

OUTRIGGER FOUNDATION AREAS ON GRANULAR SOILS

Try 2 no. layers of sleepers:

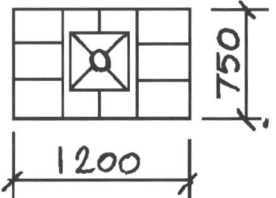

750

1200

TIMBER SLEEPERS:

③

Properties:

Section : nominal 250 × 125 (on flat)
Moment of resistance : 10·3 kNm
Shear capacity : 45·7 kN
Permissible bearing stress : 5·0 N/mm²

Upper layer : 2 no. sleepers @ 750 mm long.

0·4 m

0·75 m

Bearing stress under
outrigger pad $= \dfrac{330 \times 10^3}{400 \times 400}$

$= 2·1 \text{ N/mm}^2 \ (<5·0)$

Load per sleeper $= \dfrac{330}{2} = 165 \text{ kN}$

$M_{max} \text{ (at } \mathcal{C}) = \dfrac{165}{2} \times \dfrac{·75}{4} - \dfrac{165}{2} \times \dfrac{·4}{4}$

$= \dfrac{165}{8} \times (·75 - ·4) = \underline{7·2 \text{ kNm}} \ (<10·3)$

$S_{max} \text{ (at face of outrigger pad)}$
$= \dfrac{165}{0·75} \times \dfrac{(·75 - ·4)}{2} = \underline{38·5 \text{ kN}} \ (<45·7)$

③   For derivation of properties see page 95 of this guide

<u>Lower Layer</u> : 3 no. sleepers @ 1200 mm long :

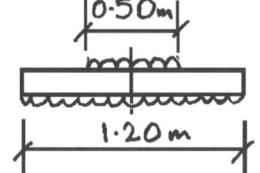

Bearing stress :
  by inspection, less
  than on upper sleepers

Load per sleeper $= \frac{330}{3} = 110 \, kN$

M_{max} (at $\text{\textcent}$) $= \frac{110}{2} \times \frac{1.2}{4} - \frac{110}{2} \times \frac{0.5}{4}$

$\qquad = \frac{110}{8} \times (1.2 - 0.5) = \underline{\underline{9.6 \, kNm}} \, (<10.3)$

S_{max} (at face of upper sleepers)

$\quad = \frac{110}{1.2} \times \frac{(1.2 - 0.5)}{2} \quad = \underline{\underline{32.1 \, kN}} \, (<45.7)$

i.e. proposed sleeper mat is satisfactory.

— Use 2 no. layers of sleepers :
   upper layer :   2 no. @ 750 mm long   on
   lower layer :   3 no. @ 1200 mm long,
   to form 750 × 1200 mm mat.
   Sleepers to be placed tightly side by side,
   and well bedded on the ground.

> **"Whilst our successes may make us clever, only failures make us wise"**   ......anon

STUDY 1   TOWER CRANE COLLAPSE

Most tower crane instability incidents occur during erection or dismantling. However, in 1991 a tower crane collapsed in a city centre while carrying out its normal duties.

The crane fell across a normally busy dual carriageway causing extensive damage not only to the building under construction but also to buildings on the other side of the road.

Due to a lucky combination of circumstances no one was killed and the only serious injury was suffered by the driver of the tower crane.

Investigations showed that collapse had occurred because of the failure of bolts connecting members in a steel grillage which supported the crane mast.

Despite good procedures being in place on site, a design detailing fault had occurred which resulted in inadequate size/number of bolts being provided at the connections. The design checker had failed to pick up this fault as he had not received the final fabrication drawings.

The crane had been in use for six months prior to the collapse and the weak connections had suffered fatigue resulting in fracture. It is believed that two bolts had fractured some weeks before the collapse, but this had gone unnoticed.

The collapse occurred when no load was being lifted, the weight of the counterweight pulling the crane over backwards.

Lessons to be learned:

- The tower crane foundation design must be properly translated into the drawings and details issued to site for construction.
- The design checker must thoroughly check all the drawings and details issued to site for construction.
- Communication between all parties and adequate document control are both very important.
- The out-of-service loading case for tower cranes can be the most severe.
- Regular inspections can pick up faults before they result in disaster.

STUDY 2   CRAWLER CRANE OVERTURNING

On a road contract a 40 tonne crawler crane toppled over, while lifting a precast beam, when the made-up-ground under one track gave way. Fortunately no one was injured but extensive damage was caused to both the crane and the works under construction.

The precast beams were delivered on Sunday and due to be lifted into position on Monday morning. Work on the hardstanding for the crane was scheduled to be done over the weekend but was not completed. On Monday morning the senior general foreman, who had pre-planned the lift, had problems with his car and was, therefore, not on site.

Although the lift had been pre-planned nothing had been committed to paper and the team involved in the operation had not been briefed.

Prior to lifting the 17 tonne precast beam, which was close to the maximum safe working load, there was disagreement between the crane driver, section foreman and sub-agent as to whether excavator mats would be needed under the crane tracks; In the event they were not used.

Lessons to be learned:

- Each lift must be supervised by one person who understands the operation and has been involved in, or fully briefed on, the pre-planning.

- All persons involved in a lifting operation must be given instructions.

- A firm, level hardstanding is required for crawler crane operations. Prior to carrying out a lift, checks must be made to ensure any required preparation work has been properly carried out.

- Pre-planning should be committed to paper including details of any ground improvements or additional spreader mats required.

STUDY 3   CRAWLER CRANE OVERTURNING

An 80 tonne crawler crane, rigged with a 30m long jib was transporting a 10 tonne load along a temporary access road when the crane overturned.

The incident resulted from poor management controls which failed to ensure the construction of a firm level access or a suitable method for transporting materials.

No assessment had been carried out to identify the risks associated with crane operations in an area above a busy highway and no actions had been taken to eliminate these risks.

The HSE Inspector stated: "It must be considered to be a matter of luck that the crane jib and load fell within the confines of the canal, that no person was hurt and that no damage occurred to traffic using the busy highway below."

Lessons to be learned:

- A careful assessment of all crane operations should be carried out

- All operations above or adjacent to highways, buildings occupied by persons, pedestrian footways etc, should be so planned that no loads are lifted over any persons and so that no failure of the crane jib can be permitted to foul such highways, buildings or pedestrian footpaths.

- All foundations for use by cranes should be level, well compacted and drained in order to ensure that no settlement occurs beneath the crane.

- Specific arrangements are necessary regarding the handling and transporting of materials and plant around site.

- Persons must be appointed to plan and monitor all lifting operations.

- Personnel training is essential and must include the safe operation and control of cranes.

STUDY 4   LORRY-MOUNTED CRANE OVERTURNING

In 1990 a 40 tonne mobile crane overturned onto an office block in a city centre.

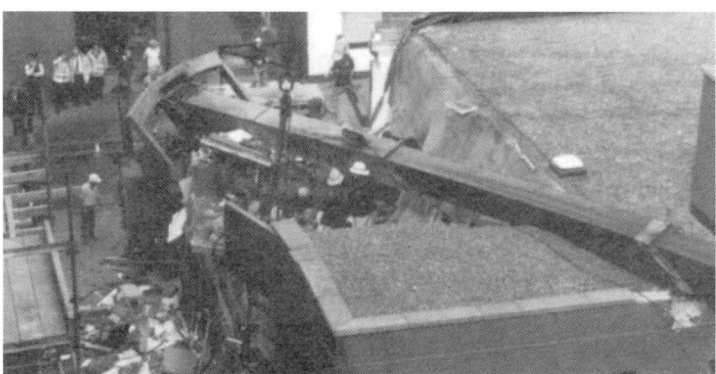

The crane was being used during the construction of a car park and was involved in lifting 1.5 tonne skips of concrete from the rear of the crane at street level and slewing to the point of pour. The load was within the capacity of the crane at the radius at which it was being operated, but the crane started to tip towards the offices and continued overturning until it came to rest supported by the building, after destroying a major proportion of the first floor.

It appears that when the crane had been used on a previous occasion, it had been set up with the outrigger pads on the footpath. However the pads had sunk into the footpath surfacing indicating that it was not capable of supporting the load.

On this occasion the crane was set up with the pads on the road offering the crane better support and not obstructing the walkway. However, the beams from the outriggers could not be fully extended as the crane would then have obstructed the road and caused major disruption to traffic.

The accident was caused by using the crane without the outrigger beams being fully extended which drastically reduced the stability of the crane.

Lessons to be learned:

- All lifts should be thoroughly assessed and planned to ensure that they can be carried out safely and that all foreseeable risks have been identified.

- The planning and risk assessment must take account of proximity hazards, space availability and suitability of ground foundations.

- There should be no ad hoc changes to the agreed plan and method statement without careful thought as these can introduce new hazards.

- Truck-mounted mobile cranes must be used with the outriggers set in accordance with the manufacturer's instructions.

Bibliography

Note: All references are correct at time of going to press but you are advised to check on their currency at time of use – particularly in the case of regulations and standards

ACTS OF PARLIAMENT AND STATUTORY INSTRUMENTS

The Health & Safety at Work, etc, Act 1974
The Construction (Design and Management) Regulations 1994
The Construction (Design and Management) (Amendment) Regulations 2000
The Construction (Health, Safety and Welfare) Regulations 1996
The Lifting Operations and Lifting Equipment Regulations 1998
The Health and Safety (Safety Signs and Signals) Regulations 1996
The Management of Health and Safety at Work Regulations 1999
The Provision and Use of Work Equipment Regulations 1998
The Supply of Machinery (Safety) Regulations 1992
The Supply of Machinery (Safety) (Amendment) Regulations 1994

BRITISH STANDARDS

BS 449:	Specification for the use of structural steel in building (permissible stress): Part 2: Metric units
BS 1377:	Methods of test for soils for civil engineering purposes
BS 1757:	Specification for power-driven mobile cranes
BS 2573:	Rules for the design of cranes: Part 1: Structures
BS 2799:	Specification for power-driven tower cranes for building and engineering construction *(Obsolescent)*
BS 5268:	Structural use of timber: Part 2: Code of practice for permissible stress design, materials and workmanship
BS 5930:	Code of practicc for site investigations
BS 5950:	Structural Use of Steelwork in Building (Limit State)
BS 5975:	Code of practice for falsework
BS 6399:	Loading for buildings: Part 1: Code of practice for dead and imposed loads
BS 6399:	Loading for buildings: Part 2 : Code of practice for wind loads
BS 7121:	Code of practice for safe use of cranes: Part 1: General
BS 7121:	Code of practice for safe use of cranes: Part 2: Inspection, testing and examination
BS 7121:	Code of practice for safe use of cranes: Part 3: Mobile cranes
BS 7121:	Code of practice for safe use of cranes: Part 4: Lorry loaders
BS 7121:	Code of practice for safe use of cranes: Part 5: Tower cranes
BS 7262:	Specification for automatic safe load indicators
BS 8004:	Code of practice for foundations
BS 8110:	Structural use of concrete
CP 3010:	Code of practice for safe use of cranes (mobile cranes, tower cranes and derrick cranes) *(Note: CP3010 is gradually being superseded by the phased issue of BS 7121)*

110

Bibliography

INTERNATIONAL STANDARDS

ISO 4304:	Cranes: General requirements for stability
ISO 4305:	Mobile cranes: Determination of stability
FEM 1.001:	Rules for the design of hoisting appliances

HSE PUBLICATIONS

HS(G) 150:	Health and Safety in construction. HMSO 2001
HS(G) 224:	Managing Health and Safety in Construction: Construction (Design and Management) Regulations 1994: Approved Code of Practice. HMSO 2001
GS 6:	Avoidance of Danger from Overhead Electric Power Lines. HMSO 1997
HS(G) 47:	Avoiding Danger from Underground Services. HMSO 2000
L113:	Safe Use of Lifting Equipment: Lifting Operations and Lifting Equipment Regulations, 1998: Approved Code of Practice and Guidance. HMSO 1998

CIRIA PUBLICATIONS

SP151:	Site Guide: Site Safety 2001
SP136:	Site Guide: Foundation Construction 1996

CITB PUBLICATIONS

GE700:	Construction Site Safety – Health, Safety and Environmental Information
PL006:	Crane Appreciation Training Notes
PSN01:	Safe Operation of Plant and Equipment
PL014:	Plant Training Notes – Crawler Cranes

CPA PUBLICATIONS

Mobile Crane Operators Safety guide. 2001
Best Practice Guide on Inspection, Thorough Examination and Maintenance of Cranes.

OTHER PUBLICATIONS

An investigation into crane accident, their causes and repair costs
Butler AJ: BRE paper 75/78

Construction Safety Manual
Construction Industry Publications Ltd *(updated yearly)*

The Crane Handbook
Dickie & Short: UK edition: Butterworth *(out of print)*

Cranes and Derricks
Shapiro: 3rd edition 1991: McGraw-Hill

Code of Practice for the Safe Use of Lifting Equipment
Lifting Equipment Engineers Association

Construction Methods and Planning
Illingworth 2nd edition 2000: E & F Spon

Mobile Crane Manual
Dickie & Hudson: UK edition 1985: Butterworth *(out of print)*

Useful Contacts

Association of Lorry Loader Manufacturers and Importers
14 Manor Close
DROITWICH WR9 8HG
Tel: 07071 226773

ALLMI Training Limited
PO Box 362
HARROGATE HG1 5UY
Tel: 01423 709809
Email: enquiries@allmitraining.co.uk

British Standards Institution (BSI)
389 Chiswick High Road
LONDON W4 4AL
Tel: 020 8996 9000
Fax: 020 8380 5555
Email: cservices@bsi-global.com
Web site: www.bsi-global.com

Building Research Establishment (BRE)
Garston
WATFORD WD25 9XX
Tel: 01923 664000
Email: enquiries@bre.co.uk
Web site: www.bre.co.uk

Construction Confederation
Construction House
56-64 Leonard Street
LONDON EC2A 4JX

Tel: 020 7608 5000
Fax: 020 7608 5001

Email: enquiries@thecc.org.uk
Website: www.constructionconfederation.co.uk

Construction Industry Training Board (CITB)
Head Office
Bircham Newton
KING'S LYNN
Norfolk PE31 6RH
Tel:01485 577577
Fax: 01485 577280
Email: information.centre@citb.co.uk
Web site: www.citb.co.uk

Useful Contacts

Construction Plant-hire Association (CPA)
27/28 Newbury Street
Barbican
LONDON EC1A 7HU
Tel: 020 7796 3366
Fax: 020 7796 3399
Email: enquiries@cpa.uk.net
Web site: www.cpa.uk.net

Construction Equipment Association
Orbital House
85 Croydon Road
CTERHAM
Surrey CR3 6PD,
Tel: 01883 334499
Fax: 01883 334490
Email: cea@admin.co.uk
Web site: fmcec.org.uk

Health and Safety Executive (HSE)
(Local offices as listed in Yellow Pages or on the HSE web site)
Tel: HSE Infoline 08701 545500
Web site: www.hse.gov.uk

Lifting Equipment Engineers Association
Waggoners Court
77, The Street
Manuden
BISHOP'S STORTFORD
Herts CM23 1DW
Tel: 01279 – 816504
Fax: 01279 – 816524
Web site: www.leea.co.uk

Safety Assessment Federation
Nutmeg House
60 Gainsford Street
Butlers Wharf
LONDON SE1 2NY
Tel: 020 7403 098
Fax: 020 7403 0137
Email: info@safed.co.uk
Web site: www.safed.co.uk

Glossary of Terms

Appointed Person	Person appointed by the Employing Organisation to have overall control of the lifting operations. The Appointed Person should have adequate training and experience to enable him/her to carry out his/her duties competently.
Ballast	Dead weight built-in or added to the structure of a crane to ensure stability.
Base	The part of the crane structure that transmits the loads and forces generated by the crane into the foundation or building structure.
Cohesive soils	Fine soils where more than 35% of the particles are finer than 0.06 mm. (clays, silts) (BS 5930 : 1981)
Counterweight	Weights added to a crane in such a position as to provide a counterbalancing effect.
Crane	A machine incorporating an elevated structural member or jib beneath which suspended loads can be controllably raised or lowered vertically and also moved horizontally either by slewing the crane, derricking the jib or by other means not solely involving a travelling motion of the crane.
Crane Driver (Operator)	The person who is operating the crane for the purpose of positioning loads or for rigging of the crane.
Derricking	See "Luffing".
Dynamic load	Load resulting from the movement of the crane and any load.
Employing Organisation	The organisation requiring a load to be moved.
External climbing crane	A tower crane external to a building or structure which can be extended in height by means of a climbing frame which jacks up the top of the crane, allowing additional sections to be inserted in the tower.
Floating counterweight	An additional counterweight suspended from the mast of a crane to increase its lifting capacity.
Floor climbing crane	A tower crane which is supported by the building or structure within which it stands, and which can be raised as the number of storeys increases.

Glossary of Terms

Fly jib	A detachable auxiliary jib fitted at the end of the jib.
Foundation	A structure which forms the interface across which loads and forces are transmitted from the base to the underlying soil or rock.
Free-on-wheels	The operational condition of a wheel mounted crane when supported solely by its wheels and able to handle appropriate loads without requiring the use of outriggers.
Granular soil	Coarse soils where less than 35% of the particles are finer than 0.06 mm. (sands, gravels) (BS 5930 : 1981)
Hoisting	The motion of lifting or lowering of a load in a vertical direction.
In-service	With the crane handling loads up to its safe working load in permissible wind speeds and other conditions as specified by the manufacturer.
Lift and Carry	The operational condition of a wheel mounted crane when supported solely by its wheels and able to handle *and travel with* appropriate loads without requiring the use of outriggers.
Luffing	Angular movement of the crane jib in a vertical plane.
Luffing fly jib	A fly jib capable of being luffed (normally with the main jib fixed at minimum radius).
Margin of stability	When the crane is handling any safe working load at the appropriate radius, the margin of stability is the additional load, expressed as a percentage of the safe working load, which is required to bring the crane to a condition of tipping with the jib adjusted as necessary to maintain the same operating radius.
Method statement	A document recording the outcomes of the risk assessment and planning process required to achieve a safe system of work.
Multiple lift	Lifting a load with two or more cranes
Operator	See "Crane Driver".

Glossary of Terms

Outriggers	Extendible structural members on the crane chassis to increase the effective base on which the crane stands.
Outrigger pad (float)	A plate like structure which forms part of the crane and which is designed to transfer forces between the crane's outrigger and the supporting surface.
Out-of-level	The angular displacement of the crane to the horizontal.
Out-of-radius	When the maximum permitted radius for a given Safe Working Load is exceeded.
Out-of-service	With the crane either not required for use or out of use, without load on the load lifting attachment and in conditions as specified by the manufacturer.
Oversailing	Where the jib of a crane (normally a tower crane) passes over an area, crane or building. This is normally of significance with railways, roads, adjoining properties etc.
Permanent Works Designer	The engineer responsible for the design of the building or structure under construction.
Pick and Carry	See "Lift and Carry"
Radius	The horizontal distance between the point at which the centre of rotation of the crane meets the ground and the vertical centreline passing through the load lifting attachment.
Rigging (Erection)	The assembly on site of a tower, crawler or large mobile crane from a number of components.
Safe Working Load (SWL)	The maximum load that can be safely handled by a crane at a specified position and under specified conditions.
Slewing	Rotary motion of a crane jib and superstructure about a vertical axis.
Tag lines	Ropes which may be fastened to a crane hook attachment to restrain spinning of the attachment.
Tandem lift	A multiple lift carried out with two cranes.
Wind load	The forces produced by the velocity of the wind, which is assumed to act horizontally.

Subject Index

Index

Index